BIG MOLECULES

Sir Harry Melville

New York

THE MACMILLAN COMPANY

Printed in the United States of America

First printing

Library of Congress Catalog Card Number: 58-12856

CONTENTS

CHAPTER

* 1 *

MAKING BIG MOLECULES

The Role of Big Molecules in Everyday Life

FOR over a hundred years chemists have been concerned with the behaviour of small molecules, and by means of all sorts of methods much has been discovered about them. Small molecules in the present sense consist perhaps of 2–50 atoms. There are many familiar examples. In the water molecule, for example, the two hydrogen atoms are joined to the oxygen atom to form a Y shaped molecule, H/O\H. In carbon dioxide the atoms CO_2 are all in a row, O=C=O. With sulphuric acid, H_2SO_4, the structure is

```
HO     O
  \   //
    S
  /   \\
HO     O
```

Such small molecules exist as gases, liquids or crystalline solids. There is, however, a large variety of substances which cannot so conveniently be classified into these three types, for example, fibres, like wool and cotton, and rubber. In addition, there are many glasslike resins which can hardly be called solids, for when they are heated they soften and eventually become thick or viscous liquids and not mobile fluids. All these substances consist of collections of large molecules, and the special properties shown by such substances are due mainly to the structure of the molecules comprising them.

All fibres, whether natural or artificial, come into this category. Wool, hair, bristles, cotton, flax, jute, animal muscle, rayon, nylon, Terylene, though very different in chemical structure, form fibres of roughly comparable strength. It is evident that some common factor must impart fibre-forming properties to these materials. In the same way natural rubber and all the synthetic rubbers, usually made from petroleum as a starting material, are made from big molecules. While the mechanical properties are very different from fibres, in that they show high extensibility or rubberiness, the basic chemical structure is similar to the fibre-forming materials. Later on it will be seen that there is not so much difference between the two types, and often one can be converted into the other by relatively simple chemical treatment.

Besides these two groups there are natural and synthetic resins, which are distinguished by the property of softening under heat and pressure so as to flow slowly like a liquid, but when heat and pressure are removed they revert again to the solid state. Perhaps the most familiar types go by the name of Perspex (a clear, glass-like resin), polyvinyl chloride, or p.v.c. for short, which is used extensively for making waterproofs, and polystyrene, which is used widely for making plastic toys and many other domestic articles.

Again, most of the solutions used for paint and varnish films, whether derived from natural or artificial sources, consist of big molecules.

The structure of materials from many living organisms is also built from substances which consist of big molecules. Most of the food we eat—flour, meat, vegetables—are all materials consisting of comparatively large molecules.

Similarly, wood, coal and pitch come under this classification.

The fact is that big molecules are not only widespread in nature, but the chemist, by artificial or synthetic means, has been able to add enormously to the variety of these materials. With this knowledge the time has come now for the chemist to make big molecules to fit specific requirements.

The reason that there is now so much interest in artificial substances is simply because it is only in the past twenty years or so that the basic knowledge of how to make and manipulate such materials has been obtained and has made possible the enormous advances in this branch of chemistry.

The Making of Big Molecules

Most big molecules have carbon as one of the essential elements in their structure. In fact, it is mainly due to the behaviour of the carbon atom that it is possible to build up such complex structures, and it is, consequently, important to see how carbon behaves when present in small molecules so as to understand how it is possible to build up much larger structures.

Carbon can combine with a number of other elements. In particular, it combines with hydrogen, and the simplest compound is methane, in which four hydrogen atoms are combined with one carbon atom and the structure is a tetrahedral one with the four hydrogen atoms at the corners and the carbon atom at the middle equally spaced from the four hydrogens, thus

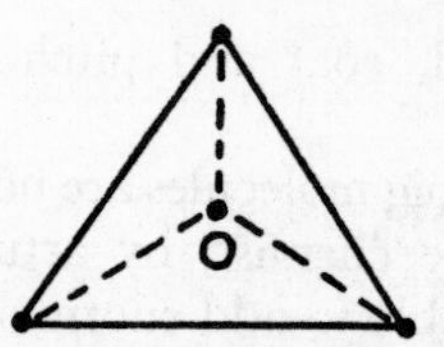

● position of centre of hydrogen atoms.
○ position of centre of carbon atom.
A Methane molecule magnified 100,000,000 times.

A slightly more complicated molecule may be made if two carbon atoms are joined together. This leaves three links for attachment to the other atoms such as

```
H\         /H
H—C—C—H
H/         \H
```

hydrogen to form the structure C_2H_6, or ethane. This type of process can be repeated and three carbon atoms joined in a row to give the molecule C_3H_8, or propane.

```
    H   H   H
    |   |   |
H—C—C—C—H
    |   |   |
    H   H   H
```

This process can further be repeated adding one carbon atom after another, thus making a long backbone of carbon atoms to each of which there is attached two hydrogen atoms except at the end of the molecule, where there would be three.

```
    H   H   H   H   H   H   H   H   H   H   H   H
    |   |   |   |   |   |   |   |   |   |   |   |
H — C — C — C — C — C — C — C — C — C — C — C — C — H
    |   |   |   |   |   |   |   |   |   |   |   |
    H   H   H   H   H   H   H   H   H   H   H   H
```

Substances containing less than five carbon atoms are gases, from five to eleven liquids and above twenty carbons atoms they tend to be solids like paraffin wax. The molecules of paraffin wax are small in the present sense of the term. However, by processes which will be mentioned later, it is possible to join many thousands of carbon atoms into a long chain. The substance so formed is still similar in a way to paraffin wax, but instead of melting to a mobile liquid as does paraffin wax, it melts above about 110° C. to a viscous liquid.

Besides linking the carbon atoms into a linear chain, another kind of structure may be thought of. If one

```
    H   H   H   H   H   H   H
    |   |   |   |   |   |   |
H — C — C — C — C — C — C — C — H
    |   |   |   |   |   |   |
    H   H   H   |   H   H   H
                |
            H — C — H
                |
            H — C — H
                |
            H — C — H
                |
                H
```

hydrogen atom is removed from one of the CH_2 groups in the middle of the chain and at that point a carbon atom joined on, a branched-chain structure is developed. The resulting material is similar to the straight-chain molecule in chemical composition, but melts at a slightly lower temperature and is a little softer to the touch.

There is, finally, a third kind of structure in which two hydrogen atoms are removed from neighbouring

```
C—C—C—C—C—C—C—C
        |
C—C—C—C—C—C—C—C
```

(The hydrogen atoms are not shown in this structure.)

groups in two adjacent long-chain molecules. The carbon atoms can then be directly joined together. If this process is carried out a number of times rings of atoms will be formed and the molecule can become very large indeed. If this process is continued until all the hydrogen atoms are removed there will remain pure carbon. If all the four links of the carbon are effectively employed in this linking-up process the resulting material is a clear crystalline solid—diamond. There are therefore three kinds of big molecules to be considered: the straight variety, the branched variety and the cross-linked variety, as they might conveniently be called for the present discussion.

The question now arises at what point a molecule is considered to be big. There is, of course, no precisely defined point at which a line may be drawn between large and small molecules, but for practical purposes a molecule is big when it gives rise to substances which possess resinous, rubbery or fibre-like properties. This usually occurs when about 200 atoms form the backbone of the chain. Even so such a molecule when stretched is only a millionth of an inch long, so it is still a very tiny fragment of matter, weighing only about 10^{-20} * of a gram.

Large molecules consisting only of carbon and hydrogen of the type described above have a very restricted range of properties—they are resins rather than rubbers or fibres. How, then, can we modify the chemical structure so as to obtain substances with quite different properties? The first modification consists of replacing some of the hydrogens by other atoms while retaining the backbone structure intact:

```
   C   C   C   C
   |   |   |   |
C—C—C—C—C—C—C—C
   |   |   |   |
   C   C   C   C
```

(The hydrogen atoms are not shown in this structure.)

For example, if the two hydrogen atoms attached to alternate carbon atoms are replaced by two CH_3 groups, a material is obtained which when suitably treated gives the artificial rubber known as butyl,† which is used for the inner tubes of car tyres because it retains the air in the tube much longer than other types of rubber. Another simple modification consists in replacing one hydrogen atom by a chlorine atom on each alternate carbon atom. This gives rise to a stiff synthetic resin known as polyvinyl chloride, which is used nowadays for making chemical plant, since it is extremely resistant to corrosive liquids and gases.

Yet a further modification consists in replacing one hydrogen atom again in each alternate carbon atom by

* 10^{-20} is a convenient way of writing the very small number

$$\frac{1}{100{,}000{,}000{,}000{,}000{,}000{,}000}.$$

† There is in addition a slight modification to the structure to make it possible to vulcanise the rubber.

a fragment of the water molecule OH, thus giving the structure

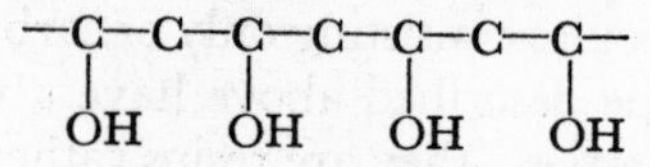

When this is done the big molecule, being partly water-like in character, has an affinity for water and actually dissolves in it to form a thick solution. The solution can be used as a size, during the manipulation of textile fibres, since it can easily be removed later on by simple washing procedures. The material itself is rather horn-like to the touch, but it can be made soft and slightly extensible if it is mixed with glycerine. The glycerine is so well incorporated that there is little tendency for it to ooze out and be lost in any way. This substance is called polyvinyl alcohol and can be drawn into fibres, but of course such fibres are useless as such because of their solubility in water. By suitable chemical treatment, however, to link the chains together, this solubility can be prevented, and textile fibres have been made from this particular type of substance.

Somewhat slightly more complicated replacement of the hydrogen atoms in the backbone can give rise to glass-clear rigid resins of a great variety of types. These materials can be used to interleave with sheets of glass to give safety windscreens and windows for motor cars. The resins themselves in greater thickness can be used as a substitute for glass where lightness is an advantage, and for many other purposes. In this case, however, the structure is a good deal more complicated, and in general it is necessary to use some oxygen atoms in the attached groups to give the desired properties. The structure of the repeating structural unit in Perspex for example is shown at the top of the next page.

```
           H
           |
       H—C—H
     H     |
     |     |
    —C—C ——> Backbone chain of carbon atoms
     |     |
     H    C=O
           |
           O
           |
       H—C—H
           |
           H
```

Not all big molecules consist of a chain of carbon atoms. Other atoms, such as oxygen, nitrogen and even silicon, also have the property of joining on to other atoms and under suitable conditions can be incorporated into the structure of big molecules. This is true of many synthetic materials, such as nylon, Terylene, phenol-formaldehyde (Bakelite) resins, urea resins and many others. Some of these structures are very complicated, but in the case of Terylene and nylon the same principles apply of building long chains of atoms in order to get fibre-forming properties from the substance. Here, however, another requirement must be met. Fabrics made from these materials must be capable of being ironed at a reasonable temperature, so it is important to have substances which will withstand temperatures of 250–300° C. without melting.

The structure of the repeating unit in nylon is as follows:

```
 H  H  H  H  O  H  H  H  H  H  H  H  O
 |  |  |  |  ||  |  |  |  |  |  |  |  ||
—C—C—C—C—C—N—C—C—C—C—C—C—N—C—
 |  |  |  |           |  |  |  |  |  |
 H  H  H  H           H  H  H  H  H  H
```

It will be seen that the whole sequence of carbon atoms in the chains is broken very occasionally by putting in one nitrogen atom. Nitrogen, however, is different from carbon, in that it can only attach itself to three hydrogen atoms, and so in this case, when it forms part of a chain, only one hydrogen atom is needed instead of two, as with carbon. Another modification to the structure in this particular case is the replacement of two hydrogen atoms on one of the carbon atoms by a single oxygen atom because one oxygen atom can attach itself to two hydrogens, as in the case of water. These slight modifications make a tremendous difference to the properties of the material and especially to the melting point; whereas a chain of carbon and hydrogen atoms gives a substance melting at about 120° C., nylon melts at 260° C. This is because the groups of $-\overset{\overset{O}{\|}}{C}-\overset{\overset{H}{|}}{N}-$ atoms attract each other very strongly indeed, so it is not easy to move the chains past each other, as happens with the pure hydrocarbon molecules when the temperature is raised.

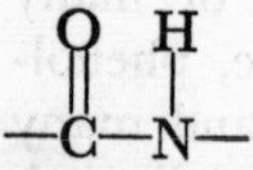

The structure of the repeating unit of Terylene is:

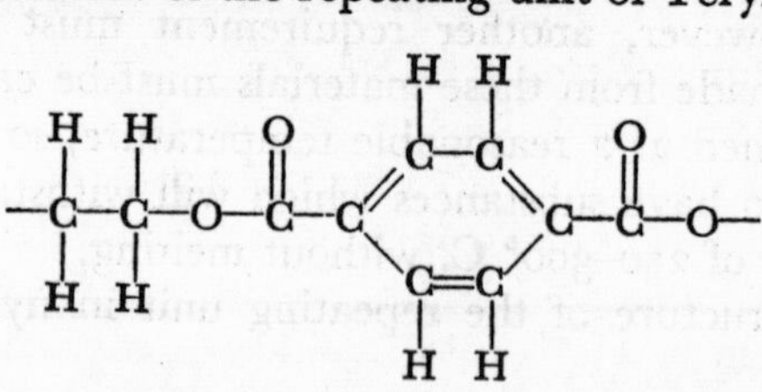

```
                        H   H
   H   H      O         |   |          O
   |   |      ‖         C — C          ‖
 — C — C — O — C — C //      \\ C — C — O —
   |   |            \\       //
   H   H              C == C
                      |    |
                      H    H
```

Here instead of a nitrogen atom there is an oxygen atom, but since oxygen is bivalent (attached to only two hydrogens normally, as in water), it takes part in the structure of the chain without requiring the addition of any hydrogen atoms to it. The other peculiar modification is the incorporation of a ring of carbon atoms. This is a very rigid unit and has an important effect on the properties of Terylene. Thus a limited introduction of small atoms, such as oxygen and nitrogen, can be used to modify the properties of a big molecule in desired directions.

Sulphur is analogous in many ways to oxygen and it can take part in chain structures, thus:

```
   H  H     H  H
   |  |     |  |
 —C—C—S—C—C—
   |  |     |  |
   H  H     H  H
```

Even two sulphur atoms can replace two carbon atoms. Such substances are either rigid resins or rubbers and are known as thiokols. They are specially resistant to solution in petroleum solvents and can be used for making hose-pipes for the handling of petroleum products.

The only other element of importance in the make-up of big molecules is silicon. It is similar to carbon in that it can combine with four atoms of hydrogen, forming SiH_4, which is a gas, or alternatively with two oxygen atoms, forming SiO_2, which is found as quartz crystal and is the main component of silver sand. The structure of quartz is not nearly so simple as the above formula would imply, for the substance does not exist as discrete unit of SiO_2. The structure is similar to diamond in that it consists of a three-dimensional array of silicon and oxygen atoms, each silicon atom being linked to four oxygen atoms, the oxygen atoms being shared between the silicon atoms. Such a structure is very rigid and of no special interest in the present connection. Other atoms may be attached to silicon, and in this way the rigid three-dimensional structure may be broken down. In particular, carbon atoms can be joined directly to a silicon atom into the following kind of structure:

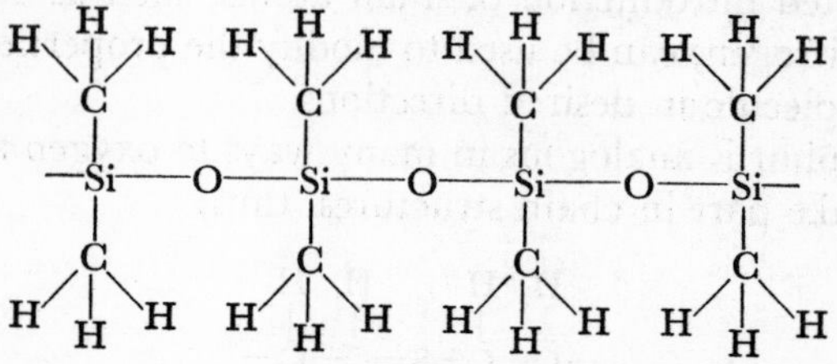

```
    H         H         H         H
 H  |  H   H  |  H   H  |  H   H  |  H
  \ | /     \ | /     \ | /     \ | /
    C         C         C         C
    |         |         |         |
  —Si———O———Si———O———Si———O———Si—
    |         |         |         |
    C         C         C         C
  / | \     / | \     / | \     / | \
 H  |  H   H  |  H   H  |  H   H  |  H
    H         H         H         H
```

The presence of two carbon atoms on each silicon prevents the silicon atoms from being bound together through the medium of the oxygen atoms, as in quartz. Thus a linear molecule can be built up with the backbone of alternate silicon and oxygen atoms instead of carbon. In addition, it is possible to provide an occasional link between the chains, and this provides an important method of modifying the properties of the molecule.

Thus the bricks for building big molecules are relatively small in number, carbon, hydrogen, oxygen, nitrogen, sulphur, chlorine, fluorine and silicon, but these eight of the 100 known chemical elements are sufficient to build up most complex structures, which, when made into various materials, can perform a great variety of roles. The rules are so simple that it is literally possible to use spherical balls to represent the various atoms and to join them together with rigid mechanical links to give a very good approximation of the actual shape of the molecules comprising these materials. In this new science of big molecule building present interest is in modifying chemically the structure of these molecules in such a way as to provide materials with an enormous range of interesting chemical, physical and mechanical properties. The connection between these properties and chemical structure has only now been gradually established, to a large extent by the method of trial and error. As more knowledge accumulates the whole business becomes more scientific and precise, so that the time may come when the specification of a material may be written down and a molecule made to yield a material which will have these defined properties to very close limits.

Methods of Making Big Molecules

The next problem is to consider how these complicated structures can be built up from relatively small molecules. The process described above of simply replacing one atom by another cannot normally be satisfactorily carried out chemically. The replacement of, say, a carbon atom by an oxygen atom in the chain itself is practically impossible in normal circumstances. Likewise the process of building up the molecules unit by unit in a succession of chemical processes would never be a practical proposition. It is therefore necessary to look for simple chemical reactions that will permit all these steps to be carried out within a single reaction vessel and in a relatively short period of time.

There are two basic methods of building up complex structures. The first is analogous in a way to the process of the neutralisation of an acid by a base. If caustic soda and sulphuric acid react in water, the equation for the process may be written:

$$NaOH + HSO_4H = NaSO_4H + H_2O$$

that is, the OH part of the caustic soda and the hydrogen atom of the sulphuric acid join together to yield a molecule of water, leaving the product sodium–hydrogen sulphate. The same kind of reaction occurs with acetic acid:

$$NaOH + HO\overset{\overset{\displaystyle O}{\|}}{C}CH_3 = NaO\overset{\overset{\displaystyle O}{\|}}{C}CH_3 + H_2O$$

Besides bases there are other molecules that contain the hydroxyl group, OH. These are alcohols; the simplest of them is methyl alcohol, CH_3OH, which forms part of the mixture known as methylated spirits. Here the same kind of reaction occurs as with acetic acid and caustic soda—

$$CH_3OH + HO\overset{\overset{\displaystyle O}{\|}}{C}CH_3 = CH_3O\overset{\overset{\displaystyle O}{\|}}{C}CH_3 + H_2O$$

the product being a substance called methyl acetate. There are, however, alcohols and acids which have a more complicated structure, in that it is possible to have molecules with two alcoholic OH groups and two acid groups COOH. The simplest type of this alcohol is ethylene glycol

$$\begin{array}{l} H\diagdown \\ \quad\; C{-}OH \\ H\diagup\;| \\ H\diagdown\;| \\ \quad\; C{-}OH \\ H\diagup \end{array}$$

which is best known for its use as an antifreeze agent in motor-car radiators. In the same way there are molecules that have two acid groups. The simplest of these is a crystalline substance called oxalic acid

$$\begin{array}{l} \mathrm{O} \\ \| \\ \mathrm{C{-}OH} \\ | \\ \mathrm{C{-}OH} \\ \| \\ \mathrm{O} \end{array}$$

This acid, for a variety of reasons, is not suitable for making synthetic fibres and other similar materials. It is, however, possible to have acids in which part of a hydrocarbon chain is inserted between the acid groups. From benzene in coal tar, by a process of oxidation, an acid containing four carbon atoms between the acid groups may be prepared. It has the structure

$$\mathrm{O{=}C(OH){-}CH_2{-}CH_2{-}CH_2{-}CH_2{-}C(OH){=}O}$$

This is the acid that is used to make nylon. When such an acid reacts with an alcohol containing two alcohol groups it does so as follows:

$$\mathrm{HO{-}CH_2{-}CH_2{-}OH} + \mathrm{HO{-}\overset{\overset{\displaystyle O}{\|}}{C}{-}CH_2{-}CH_2{-}CH_2{-}CH_2{-}\overset{\overset{\displaystyle O}{\|}}{C}{-}OH}$$

$$\mathrm{HO{-}CH_2{-}CH_2{-}O{-}\overset{\overset{\displaystyle O}{\|}}{C}{-}CH_2{-}CH_2{-}CH_2{-}CH_2{-}\overset{\overset{\displaystyle O}{\|}}{C}{-}OH} + \mathrm{HOH}$$

one molecule of water being produced as a result of the reaction between the acid and the alcohol group. The important point, however, is that the bigger molecule produced in the reaction has got an alcoholic group at one end and an acid group at the other. Consequently at the alcoholic end another molecule of acid can react giving rise to a still larger molecule. Similarly at the acid end an alcohol group may react, a molecule of water being simultaneously produced. If we represent the acid by the symbol A and the alcohol by the symbol B, then the set of reactions can be set down in the following way:

$$
\begin{array}{c}
A + B \\
\downarrow \\
AB + BA \\
\downarrow \\
ABAB + ABAB \\
\downarrow \\
ABABABAB
\end{array}
$$

As we shall see later, in order to get molecules of a size that give rise to substances of fibre-forming properties, we need to build at least 100 units of A and B into the structure of the long molecule. But this does not mean that a sequence of a hundred separate chemical reactions each involving the elimination of a molecule of water must take place.

Addition of Small Molecules

There is another way in which little molecules may be joined together. On p. 12 it was pointed out that a carbon atom can become united with four hydrogen atoms, giving a molecule of methane, CH_4. If one of the hydrogen atoms is removed from the methane, as it can be at high temperatures, this gives rise to a piece of a molecule $-C{\lt}^{H}_{H}{-}H$ with one of the bonds not united to any other atom. Such a piece of a molecule is called a free radical. When two of these fragments meet each other they unite because of the existence of the free bond in the molecular fragment

```
H\          /H
H—>C—  +  —C<—H
H/          \H
       |
       ↓
H\          /H
H—>C————————C<—H
H/          \H
```

Here the two carbon atoms are joined by one link or bond. It is possible to carry the matter a stage further. If two hydrogen atoms are removed from the methane molecule there will be two unattached bonds in the molecular fragment, and when two such fragments react they give rise to a molecule called ethylene in which the two carbon atoms are joined by a double link:

```
H       H
 \     /
  C═C
 /     \
H       H
```

This link can be partly broken to give a molecule in which there are two unattached links, thus:

```
H\      /H
 —>C—C<—
H/      \H
```

When this is done two similar molecules could join up to give a unit twice the size

```
H\     H  H    /H
 —>C—C—C—C<—
H/     H  H    \H
```

still possessing the unattached link at each end. By

this means long molecules could be built up. In practice, however, it is done in quite a different way. Although molecules such as ethylene do join up to form long molecules, the reaction is not an easy one to carry out. When one or more of the hydrogen atoms in the ethylene molecule is replaced by other atoms such as chlorine, the reaction becomes very much easier. If chlorine is used the molecule is

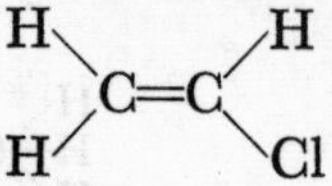

$$\begin{array}{ccc} H & & H \\ & C{=}C & \\ H & & Cl \end{array}$$

and is called vinyl chloride, which is a gas at ordinary temperatures. This is the substance used to make big molecules that go to form such things as plastic waterproofs, plastic curtains and many other familiar articles.

These molecules are induced to link up by using the following kind of idea. It was mentioned above that if a hydrogen atom is removed from methane the molecular fragment

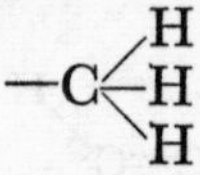

$$-C\begin{array}{l} H \\ H \\ H \end{array}$$

results. That fragment very readily attacks the vinyl chloride molecule, giving rise to a bigger molecular fragment:

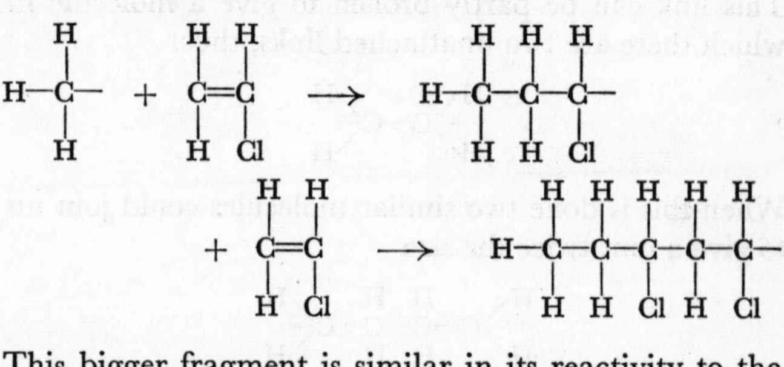

$$\begin{array}{ccccccc} & H & & H & H & & H\ \ H\ \ H \\ H{-} & C & {-}\ \ + & C{=} & C & \longrightarrow & H{-}C{-}C{-}C{-} \\ & H & & H & Cl & & H\ \ H\ \ Cl \end{array}$$

$$\begin{array}{cccc} & H\ \ H & & H\ \ H\ \ H\ \ H\ \ H \\ + & C{=}C & \longrightarrow & H{-}C{-}C{-}C{-}C{-}C{-} \\ & H\ \ Cl & & H\ \ H\ \ Cl\ \ H\ \ Cl \end{array}$$

This bigger fragment is similar in its reactivity to the small one, so it in turn attacks another vinyl chloride molecule, adding it on to form an even bigger fragment. And so the process goes on until very large numbers, up to 10,000, of these units are added on. These fragments are so reactive chemically that this great number of units can be added on in less than a tenth of a second. Here in fact we have a chain-like process, in that once the initial attack occurs the subsequent reactions occur easily and quickly. The growth does not go on indefinitely because, as we shall see in the next chapter, big molecules of a well-defined size are produced. The growth reaction itself comes to an end in some cases by two of the fragments uniting with each other to give an unreactive, big molecule.

The Chemistry of Making Big Molecules

It is easy to draw molecular structures on paper and remove and replace atoms or groups of atoms to give all sorts of different types of large molecules. It is quite a different matter to build up these molecules in practice. Further, many of the substances are required in different physical forms such as glass-clear solids, fine powders, or suspensions in water. The method of preparation must therefore be chosen to suit the end use of the substance. The simplest method is that used for the production of the glass-clear plastic known as Perspex. Not only must the solid be free from impurities, it must also possess a polished surface comparable in flatness and smoothness to that of plate glass. Although this plastic may be ground and polished, as happens in the fabrication of plate glass, a much simpler and more direct method is used to get a satisfactory surface.

The starting substance is a glass-clear mobile liquid boiling at about the same temperature as water. Its name is methyl methacrylate, having the formula

$$
\begin{array}{l}
\qquad\quad\ CH_3 \\
\qquad\ \ / \\
CH_2{=}C \\
\qquad\ \ \backslash \\
\qquad\quad\ C{-}CH_3 \\
\qquad\ \ // \\
\qquad O
\end{array}
$$

Into this liquid there is dissolved a peroxide—rather more complicated in structure than hydrogen peroxide —which splits up when heated into molecular fragments of the type CH_3. These add on to the small molecules in the manner already described, to yield molecules with about 5,000 units in their structure. During the accumulation of the product the liquid becomes thicker and thicker. While it is still in the form of a pourable syrup it is tipped into a mould made from two highly polished sheets of plate glass separated by suitable gaskets which contain the liquid and determine the thickness of the final sheet. This mould has to be ingeniously constructed so as to allow for the contraction of the syrup as it is transformed into a solid. If this is not done the solid would tend to detach itself from the glass and the surface finish of the plastic would be spoiled. This whole assembly is placed in an oven at a suitable temperature and the process allowed to go on until all the small molecules have been chemically transformed into large ones. When cool the glass is separated from the plastic, which is then ready for its manifold uses.

In carrying out such chemical reactions there are two important effects which determine the procedure in large-scale practice. The first is that the syrup becomes thicker and thicker (or more viscous) as the reaction proceeds, and the second that a considerable amount of heat is evolved during the process. This heat amounts to 130 calories per gram in the manufacture of Perspex. If it were not removed it would raise the temperature of the liquid far above its boiling point. For these two reasons it is not practicable to carry out reactions of this kind in large containers with a capacity of a ton or more, so other methods have to be devised. With some compounds a very convenient phenomenon makes it possible to keep the system fluid and to get the heat away sufficiently quickly. If we start with the molecule with one chlorine atom in it, $CH_2{=}C\begin{smallmatrix}H\\Cl\end{smallmatrix}$ (vinyl chloride), it so happens that the large molecules, or macromolecules as they are called, formed from it, are insoluble in the liquid and are therefore precipitated as a solid. Thus, a suspension is formed whose fluidity is not much less than the liquid at the start of the reaction. Because of the fluidity of the liquid it is easily stirred, and the heat can therefore be readily dissipated even in large vessels. The reaction cannot be allowed to go to completion, as the whole mass would become solid. Before this stage is reached the reaction is stopped by adding suitable chemicals and the vinyl chloride (boiling at − 10° C.) can readily be flashed off by evaporation.

Another method of getting over these difficulties consists in using the so-called 'pearl' process. Here the liquid, containing a suitable substance to start off the building-up reaction, is suspended in water as small droplets. This is practical in many cases, since the small molecules are not appreciably soluble in water. The liquid spheres gradually become solid as the reaction takes place, but retain their initial shape.

On account of the size of the spheres the heat is readily removed and the water is easily separated from the spheres at the end of the reaction to give a free-flowing powder.

The use of water as a suspending medium can be further extended to do what the rubber tree has been doing since the beginning of its existence. Many plants, for example the common dandelion, produce a so-called latex. This is a very finely divided suspension of rubber in a watery medium. In trying, therefore, to make synthetic rubber in this physical form chemists have had to investigate in some considerable detail the nature of such a suspension. In fact most of the synthetic rubber produced nowadays consists of a latex, and quite a number of other synthetic plastics are made by a similar process. The essence of the process is the presence of soap in the system. A soap molecule, whether of the traditional or of the newer synthetic variety, is a peculiar molecule in that one part of it is hydrocarbon-like in nature, and therefore insoluble in water, while the other part is soluble in water. The structure is similar to part of the hydrocarbon molecule mentioned on p. 13, and that of a simple soap molecule is as follows:

$$\mathrm{H{-}\underset{H}{\overset{H}{C}}{-}\left(\underset{H}{\overset{H}{C}}\right)_{17}{-}\overset{\displaystyle O}{\overset{\|}{C}}{-}ONa}$$

It is the salt of the same kind of acid as acetic acid, except there is a chain of carbon atoms attached to the acid part. The left-hand part of the molecule would try to dissolve in a hydrocarbon because it is in fact a hydrocarbon, while the right side of the molecule would tend to dissolve in water, as does acetic acid. It is these two opposing tendencies which give rise to the interesting properties of soap solutions. If the solution contains less than 1 % by weight of soap, the molecule exists in the state indicated above, the right-hand end being ionised to a negatively charged acid ion $CH_3(CH_2)_{17}C(=O)—O^{\ominus}$ and a positively charged sodium ion Na^+. When the solution becomes more concentrated the soap molecules tend to form bunches or aggregates, and if we represent the molecule by the symbol 〰o it is believed that the aggregates have the structure

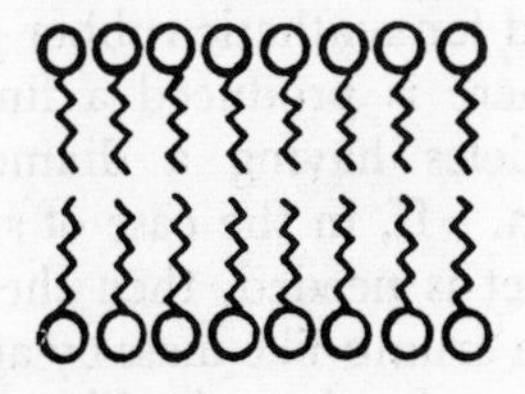

the hydrocarbon parts of the molecule fitting together. If a liquid hydrocarbon of a suitable type for making large molecules is mixed with the soap solution, it makes its way to the hydrocarbon part of the soap molecule aggregate and dissolves in it, making the whole system a little bigger. In fact it would appear that the hydrocarbon dissolves in a watery solution. Soap molecules, however, can only take up a limited amount of hydrocarbon and any excess remains suspended as an emulsion, that is to say, a dispersion in water.

It is necessary to have some means of starting off the growth of large molecules. Here we make use of molecules such as hydrogen peroxide, H—O—O—H, which are similar to water, except that two oxygen atoms are between the two hydrogen atoms. Hydrogen peroxide is not a very stable substance, for on heating it breaks up into water and oxygen. In the presence of iron salts it does so even more readily. Although oxygen and water are the final products of the reaction, the hydrogen peroxide molecule is broken up into molecular fragments, OH, in the first part of the reaction. Such a fragment collides and reacts by adding on to the hydrocarbon in the soap aggregate, and thus starts off molecular growth, as described on p. 26. As the small molecules grow into large molecules, so more are supplied from the emulsified droplets which act as reservoirs for the storage of the reactive molecules needed for synthetic rubber production. As a final result there is produced a fine suspension or latex with particles having a diameter of 1/1000–1/10000 of a mm. If, in the case of synthetic rubber, solid rubber sheet is needed, then the latex is readily coagulated into a crumb-like mass by adding acids such as sulphuric or acetic plus salts like sodium sulphate. In this form the rubber is washed free of soap and other additives, and then can be dried and pressed into sheets for further manipulation.

The latex itself can be used for making foamed rubber, or for films and threads, and modified lattices can be used for the production of emulsion paints after suitable treatment.

Some molecules, for example ethylene itself, do not give rise to big molecules by any of the variety of processes described so far. For ethylene it is necessary to compress the gas to a pressure of nearly a thousand atmospheres at a temperature of 200° C. In order to carry out this reaction a very specialised type of equipment is needed. Very pure ethylene is mixed with a tiny trace of oxygen, about 0·1 per cent. by volume. This mixture is then compressed to such an extent that it has nearly the density of a normal liquid. It then passes

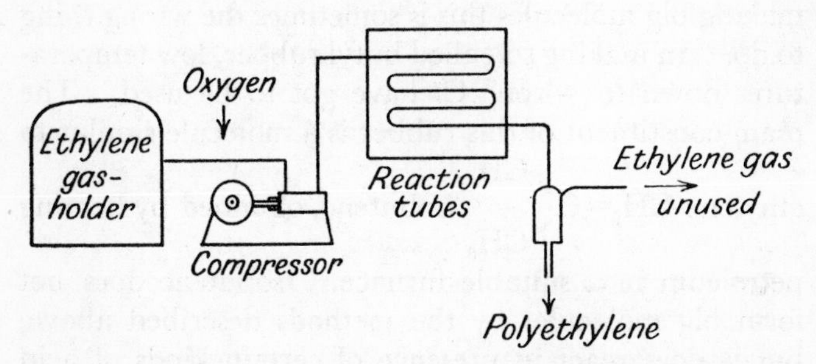

FIG. 1. Diagram for the process for the polymerisation of ethylene.

through a series of pipes, the ethylene being gradually converted into a viscous liquid, which emerges from the end of the plant and solidifies at about 110° C. This process is continuous, and the size of the pipe, the high temperature of operation and the relatively low melting point of the product make it possible to overcome the difficulties mentioned above when a system changes from a mobile to a viscous fluid.

Recently it has been found that besides using high-pressure and high-temperature methods, the unreactive ethylene molecule will join up at room temperature and atmospheric pressure when it is dissolved in a hydrocarbon liquid like petrol and brought into contact with a solid catalyst, of which there are a great many types. Here the molecules of ethylene are attached to the surface of the catalyst and at a suitable occasion are induced to join up. The big molecule is not then so strongly attached to the catalyst, and therefore it is dissolved off by the solvent in which the catalyst is suspended.

It is usual to increase the temperature to make a chemical reaction go faster, but in this business of making big molecules this is sometimes the wrong thing to do. In making so-called butyl rubber, low temperatures down to $-100°$ C. have got to be used. The main constituent of this rubber is a molecule similar to ethylene $CH_2{=}C\begin{matrix} \diagup CH_3 \\ \diagdown CH_3 \end{matrix}$ isobutene, obtained by heating petroleum in a suitable furnace. Isobutene does not form big molecules by the methods described above, but it does react in presence of certain kinds of acid which we may denote by HA. These acids, like all others, split into ions H^+ and A^-. The hydrogen ion adds on to the hydrocarbon

$$H^+ + CH_2{=}C\begin{matrix} \diagup CH_3 \\ \diagdown CH_3 \end{matrix} \longrightarrow \begin{matrix} & CH_3 \\ & | \\ CH_3{-} & C^+ \\ & | \\ & CH_3 \end{matrix}$$

$$\longrightarrow \begin{matrix} & CH_3 & & CH_3 \\ & | & & | \\ CH_3{-} & C & {-}CH_2{-} & C^+ \\ & | & & | \\ & CH_3 & & CH_3 \end{matrix}$$

and it is this positively charged larger ion that induces other small molecules to link up rapidly with it, the positive charge always being located at the end of the growing large molecule. In the production of butyl rubber the reaction is so fast that the small molecules, together with solvent and catalyst, are run in at one end of the reactor and the synthetic rubber issues from the other end ready to be manipulated into suitable sheets. In this case the reaction comes to an end by a positive hydrogen ion being removed from the growing molecule by the negative ion, and then the acid HA is ready to start off again the growth of another large molecule.

There is another important kind of resin known as a phenolic resin or appropriately by the name of Bakelite, after its discoverer, L. H. Baekeland. The chemistry of their formation is rather complicated, but the actual method used is basically quite simple. The two starting components are formaldehyde, $\underset{H}{\overset{H}{>}}C{=}O$, that is to say methane with two of the hydrogen atoms replaced by one oxygen atom, and phenol or carbolic acid. This latter molecule is rather like the alcohols referred to above, but attached to the OH group there is a more complicated structure of carbon and hydrogen atoms in which the system forms a ring with alternate single and double links in it. Since the carbon atom has four links this means that only one hydrogen is attached to each carbon atom and therefore the structure can be written:

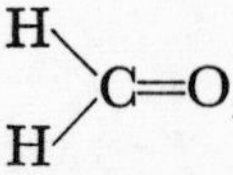

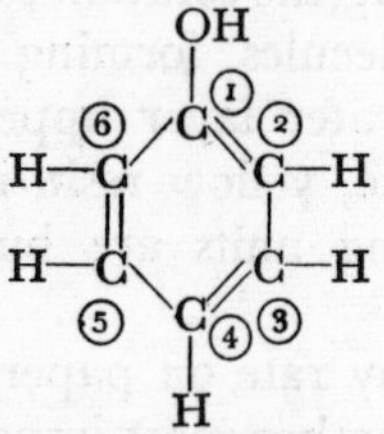

```
              OH
              |  (1)
        (6)  /C\\ (2)
     H—C          C—H
       ||         |           phenol molecule
     H—C          C—H
       (5)  \C// (3)
              | (4)
              H
```

Under the influence of a weak acid or alkali in water solution, and moderate heat up to 100° C., these two molecules react together in the following way:

```
      OH                      OH                          OH
      |                       |                           |
      C                       C                           C
   //   \                  //   \                      //   \
HC        CH + CH2O   HC        C—CH2OH + HC        CH
|         ||    ——>   |         ||                 |         ||
HC        CH          HC        CH                 HC        CH
   \\   /                \\   /                       \\   /
     CH                      CH                          CH
                                                          |
                                                          ↓
                              OH                          OH
                              |                           |
                              C                           C
                           //   \                      //   \
                      HC        C—CH2—C        CH
        H2O  +        |         ||          |         ||
                      HC        CH          HC        CH
                         \\   /                \\   /
                           CH                      CH
```

the formaldehyde thus forming another alcoholic group. But this group has the important property that it reacts readily with a hydrogen atom in another carbolic acid molecule to give a molecule of water, the other product being a molecule of larger size in which the two phenol units are linked together via a CH_2 group. Another molecule of formaldehyde can then react to yield a further alcohol group, and so the process goes on, building up a chain of similar units in the molecule. After a few minutes' heating the solution separates into two layers, the big molecules forming the lower, heavier layer, with the water layer uppermost. On cooling, a brittle, glass-like, yellow resin is formed in which the above repeating units are built into the big molecule.

There is no limit, at any rate on paper, to the size of such a molecule, but another most important factor enters into molecule building. So far we have dealt with linear long molecules, which we may represent by a zig-zag ⌇⌇⌇ of carbon atoms. The lines represent the links joining the repeating units together. But there are two possible additional kinds of structure which may be formed, those obtained by growing branches on to the straight chains thus:

and those in which the chains are joined together by cross links to give the following kind of structure:

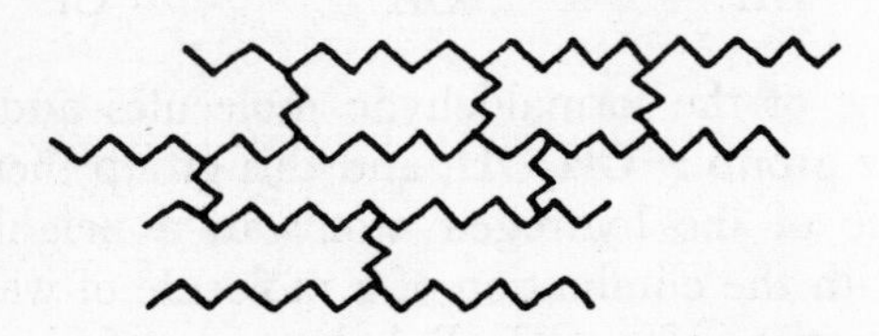

These structures give rise to materials whose properties are very different from those of linear molecules. What are the chemical methods of making this change? In the reaction between phenol and formaldehyde there are five hydrogen atoms in the phenol molecule that might react with formaldehyde. In fact only three of them in positions 2, 4 and 6 (see p. 35) actually do so; for reasons that would take too long to discuss here. If only two of the hydrogens take part in molecule-building, then linear molecules are produced, but ultimately the third atom will likewise take part, so providing the means for making cross links between the chains. A part of the cross-linking reaction is shown on the next page:

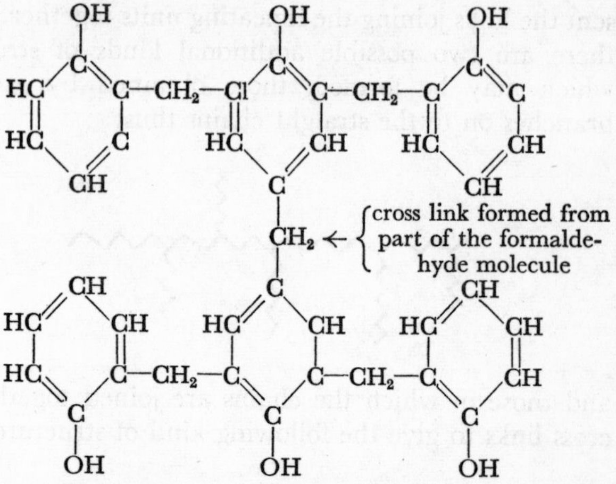

CH_2 ← cross link formed from part of the formaldehyde molecule

Here one of the formaldehyde molecules adds on to form the group $-CH_2OH$, and this group then reacts with one of the hydrogen atoms in a neighbouring chain with the elimination of a molecule of water and the formation of a CH_2 link between chains. This process occurs on heating the brittle resin with additional formaldehyde using an acid or alkaline catalyst. Whereas the brittle resin is fusible and soluble (in methylated spirits for example), the substance then becomes infusible and insoluble. The linear molecules are now held together in such a way that they cannot move about—they are immobilised by these chemical links to form what is called a heat-hardened resin. On heating to a high enough temperature, the resin ultimately decomposes into a complex variety of products. The various methods of using these resins will be described in Chapter 5. There is, however, one interesting procedure in completing the final stage of the reaction. If a large amount of catalyst is used a great deal of heat is developed quickly, which cannot easily get away because of the stickiness of the medium. At the same time the water evolved in the reaction is converted into steam, which disperses the whole mass into a solid foam. This foam consists of numerous small pockets of air dispersed in the resin and is an excellent heat insulator of very low density. It is also of use as a shock insulator, since although the resin is fairly rigid itself, this 'foamy' form of the structure is particularly effective in reducing the intensity of a shock-wave applied to it by a sudden blow from a hard object.

There is another general principle in molecule-building which is now coming into use in making certain varieties of synthetic rubber. It sometimes happens that the chemical reactions involving the building up of big molecules are such that it is impractible to go beyond a certain limit because of complicating side reactions, yet there is a need to make bigger molecules because only in that way can certain desirable mechanical properties be obtained. This is particularly the case with the reactions that are used in making nylon and Terylene. However, in these cases the ends of the molecule can be made to contain reactive groups like OH. Then it is a question of joining these not-so-big molecules into much longer ones by suitable complicated chemical reagents. The reaction can be set down as follows:

HO〰OH HO〰OH HO〰OH HO〰OH HO〰OH

linking agent(X) linking agent linking agent linking agent

HO〰〰X〰〰X〰〰X〰〰X〰〰OH

In this way a resin-like material, usually a thick liquid, can be converted into a rubber. Further, by using an excess of linking agent it is possible to link the chains while still retaining the rubber-like properties. In addition to all this, the linking agent is such that when it comes into contact with a small amount of water in the resin, carbon dioxide is evolved, and this expands the rubber into a foam which can be used as cushions, sponges and other similar articles.

These reactions of cross linking are of the utmost importance in modifying properties of molecules, but sometimes it is necessary to be able to undo and re-form cross links. Human hair consists of long molecules of a particularly complicated structure, but the cross links consist of two sulphur atoms joining long chains together. These links give the hair stability so that it does not easily change its length when wet. Similarly, when hot, hair must not be appreciably weakened when it is damp and under tension. In hot water, using pressure, straight human hair can be set into a curled shape, but of course when it is washed again in warm water the curl comes out—it is not permanent. In order to do permanent waving of hair at room temperature the principles of molecule-building may be applied. First of all the cross links have to be undone. This can be brought about by treating the hair with a solution of a substance called ammonium thioglycollate, which has the effect of breaking the links between the sulphur atoms and adding on two hydrogen atoms, as shown by the models in Plate 1*a*. In this state the hair becomes plastic and can readily be formed into any desired shape, for example by winding it tightly over a suitable former. After an hour or so the necessary number of cross links is broken. These are now re-formed in their new positions by treating the hair with a dilute solution of hydrogen peroxide and the curl is chemically built into the structure of the hair.

One can even operate this process in reverse. Some people—a minority—may wish to have their hair straightened. The same procedure is adopted, except that the hair must be kept stretched during the cutting of the cross links. When this is completed the links are re-formed so that the hair remains permanently straight.

As we shall see later, the cross-linking reactions are of great importance in the compounding of rubber, the formation of some kinds of paint films and in raising the melting points of plastics of relatively low melting point.

Silicones

While most of the big molecules that are used in practice consist of chains of carbon atoms, sometimes with an occasional oxygen or nitrogen atom, the principles of molecule-building can be applied to other elements too. Silicon, for example, is similar to carbon in that it can unite with four hydrogen atoms to form the compound SiH_4 or with two oxygen atoms to give SiO_2, the building block in common white sand and quartz. Similarly, the silicon atoms can unite with four chlorine atoms to give $SiCl_4$, silicon tetrachloride, which is a colourless liquid fuming in moist air. This fuming is due to reaction with water when all the four chlorine atoms form hydrochloric acid to give a hydrated form of silica—silica gel.

$$SiCl_4 + 4H_2O = SiO_2 2H_2O + 4HCl$$

The silica gel on heating and fusing forms SiO_2:

$$
\begin{array}{ccccc}
 & & | & & \\
 & & -Si- & & \\
 & & | & & \\
 & & O & & \\
| & & | & & | \\
-Si- & O & -Si- & O & -Si- \\
| & & | & & | \\
 & & O & & \\
 & & | & & \\
 & & -Si- & & \\
 & & | & &
\end{array}
$$

In the crystal of quartz the structure really consists of long chains of silicon and oxygen atoms, but in addition every silicon atom is linked through an oxygen atom to two other silicon atoms. This gives a very rigid structure which is not plastic except when the melting point of silica is reached at 1,350° C. This structure may be modified by means of a process discovered by Professor F. S. Kipping more than fifty years ago. Instead of starting with silicon tetrachloride, we replace two of the chlorine atoms in the silicon tetrachloride molecule by methyl groups to give the following molecule dimethyl silicon dichloride:

$$
\begin{array}{c}
CH_3 \\
| \\
Cl-Si-Cl \\
| \\
CH_3
\end{array}
$$

When this molecule reacts with water only the two chlorine atoms are removed, the first reaction being

$$
\begin{array}{c}
CH_3 \\
| \\
Cl-Si-Cl \\
| \\
CH_3
\end{array}
+ 2H_2O \longrightarrow
\begin{array}{c}
CH_3 \\
| \\
HO-Si-OH \\
| \\
CH_3
\end{array}
+ 2HCl
$$

Such molecules then begin to link up, thus:

$$HO-\underset{\underset{CH_3}{|}}{\overset{\overset{CH_3}{|}}{Si}}-OH + HO-\underset{\underset{CH_3}{|}}{\overset{\overset{CH_3}{|}}{Si}}-OH$$

$$\longrightarrow \quad HO-\underset{\underset{CH_3}{|}}{\overset{\overset{CH_3}{|}}{Si}}-O-\underset{\underset{CH_3}{|}}{\overset{\overset{CH_3}{|}}{Si}}-OH \quad + \quad H_2O$$

This process can, of course, go on indefinitely. However, it is possible to limit the growth by adding to the mixture, during the reaction with water, another type of silicon molecule which prevents further growth of the chain. This has three methyl groups and only one chlorine atom:

$$CH_3-\underset{\underset{CH_3}{|}}{\overset{\overset{CH_3}{|}}{Si}}-Cl$$

It joins on at the end of the big molecule in the following way:

$$CH_3-\underset{\underset{CH_3}{|}}{\overset{\overset{CH_3}{|}}{Si}}-O-\underset{\underset{CH_3}{|}}{\overset{\overset{CH_3}{|}}{Si}}-O-\underset{\underset{CH_3}{|}}{\overset{\overset{CH_3}{|}}{Si}}-CH_3$$

giving rise to a terminal CH_3 group. By this means it is possible to make molecules of all sizes, and in this particular case one can make mobile, clear liquids, and gels at will. Just as it is possible to vary the length of the chain, so it is possible to join the chains together by means of a cross link involving an oxygen atom. In this a small amount of a molecule containing three chlorine atoms is used:

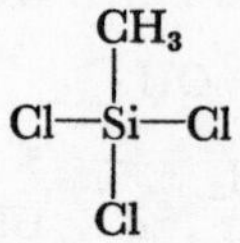

$$
\begin{array}{c}
CH_3 \\
| \\
Cl{-}Si{-}Cl \\
| \\
Cl
\end{array}
$$

This molecule on interaction with water joins in with the main chain and another molecule with a neighbouring chain so that the cross link has the following structure:

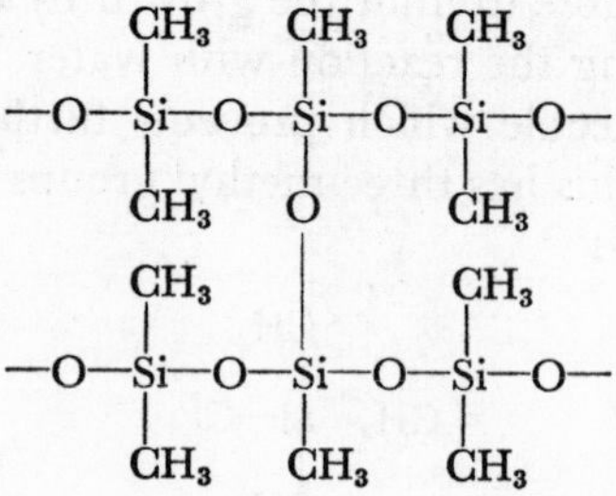

$$
\begin{array}{ccccccccccc}
 & & CH_3 & & CH_3 & & CH_3 & & \\
 & & | & & | & & | & & \\
{-}O{-} & & Si & {-}O{-} & Si & {-}O{-} & Si & & {-}O{-} \\
 & & | & & | & & | & & \\
 & & CH_3 & & O & & CH_3 & & \\
 & & & & | & & & & \\
 & & CH_3 & & | & & CH_3 & & \\
 & & | & & | & & | & & \\
{-}O{-} & & Si & {-}O{-} & Si & {-}O{-} & Si & & {-}O{-} \\
 & & | & & | & & | & & \\
 & & CH_3 & & CH_3 & & CH_3 & &
\end{array}
$$

This makes the whole structure more rigid, but not nearly so rigid as in a quartz crystal because of the infrequency of the oxygen links. The advantage in building up a structure based on silicon and oxygen is that it is more resistant to breakdown at high temperatures than is a chain of carbon atoms, and this gives the silicones special properties that will be discussed in Chapter 6.

Chemical Modifications of Big Molecules

In many cases big molecules, whether they come from natural sources or are made chemically by the kinds of reaction described above, are not really suitable for a particular application. It is necessary, therefore, to alter chemically the nature of the groups attached to the backbone without altering the backbone itself. For example, cellulose from the cotton plant, or from certain kinds of trees, can be treated with acetic acid and made into cellulose acetate, which is the raw material for a number of textile fibres having different properties from pure cellulose fibres. Similarly, natural rubber, which consists of long carbon chains, can be treated with strong sulphuric acid so that small rings of carbon atoms are formed along the main backbone, with the result that the rubber becomes much less soft. It develops, however, a great resistance to abrasion, and this makes it a specially useful material for the soles of footwear when mixed with a suitable proportion of ordinary rubber. It is called cyclised rubber because of its chemical structure.

Another example of the intentional modification of a molecule is one carried out with cellulose. Cellulose, in the form of cotton wool or wood pulp, is swollen by water, but does not dissolve in it. By treating it with chloracetic acid, $ClCH_2COOH$, which is simply acetic acid slightly modified by removing a hydrogen atom and replacing it with chlorine (thus: $Cl—CH_2—COOH$), one introduces an acid group into the cellulose molecule and the general structure is a backbone with a large number of such groups as pendant attachments. This acid can be neutralised by caustic soda, producing a modified cellulose that swells and dissolves readily in water. It has a great number of applications: one is as an adhesive for paper and similar materials, which is extensively used for hanging wallpaper; others are as a thickening agent for cosmetic creams in which water plays a part and in making ice-cream.

CHAPTER

* 2 *

THE SIZE OF BIG MOLECULES

The size of a big molecule has a profound effect on its physical and chemical properties and so it is important to measure size accurately in order that these properties may be correlated with size. In addition, during the manufacture of such substances control methods are needed to follow the course of the chemical processes involved. There are now many methods of size determination and each one of them has its own particular sphere of application. Although these molecules are big by ordinary standards, some of the biggest of them only weigh one millionth of a millionth of a millionth of a gram, or expressed in figures, 10^{-18} grams. The most sensitive balance that has ever been devised will weigh perhaps a millionth of a gram of matter, so clearly there is no hope of weighing a molecule, even if we could isolate it and place it on the pan of the most sensitive balance.

The Electron Microscope

Similarly, these molecules cannot be seen by any type of optical microscope which can only make visible particles of matter about 10 millionths of a centimetre in diameter. These big molecules have a diameter of about 1/10th of a millionth of a centimetre. The only way of observing directly such a small piece of isolated material is to use an electron microscope. Even the best electron microscope cannot detect the existence of some of the smaller big molecules, for a reason which will become clear from what follows. An electron microscope works in quite a different way from an optical microscope, but some of the general ideas are similar. A diagram of the two types is shown in figure 2. In the optical microscope the light from a lamp is focused on the object by means of a condensing lens. A magnified image of the object is formed by the objective lens, and this is further magnified by an eyepiece lens or projected by a similar kind of lens on to a photographic plate. In the electron microscope electrons are used to form the image instead of visible light. Although an electron is usually described as the smallest charge of electricity that can exist, and is in a way regarded as a particle, an electron can also exhibit wave-like properties. For example, a narrow beam of electrons can be formed in a vacuum and by means of electric or magnetic fields a divergent beam of such electrons can be focused in the same way as visible light is focused. The electron beam has, however, an immense advantage over the optical instrument, for the following reason. The seeing or resolving power of the optical microscope is governed by the wavelength of visible light which is 4×10^{-5} cm. or 40 millionths of a centimetre, in the blue region of the spectrum. So it is not practicable to discern objects much smaller than this no matter what magnification is used. The wavelength of the electrons is much smaller and it depends on the speed with which they travel. If such electrons are accelerated by subjecting them to a voltage of about 100,000 they behave as if they had a wavelength of about 1/100th of a millionth of a centimetre; and so if a suitable microscope could be constructed it should be able to 'see' big molecules individually. The source of 'light', so to speak, is a heated filament that gives off electrons. These are accelerated by potentials up to 100,000 volts, and emerge with a speed of 10^8 cm./sec. Such a beam of electrons is focused by a magnetic lens—the condenser—on to a minute apparatus for supporting the object being examined. This beam is then focused by another magnetic lens to form an enlarged image of the object. A second magnetic lens enlarges this image still further so that a second image can be formed in the plane of a photographic film, or on a fluorescent screen for visual examination. The fast electrons make it possible to take photographs in a few seconds and also illuminate the screen sufficiently brightly to be seen in a darkened room. (In the lectures at the Royal Institution the image on the screen of an electron microscope was magnified still further by a television apparatus so that a very large image was projected on the screen of a television receiver.)

The next problem is the preparation of the object. First there must be something to support the object itself. Further, this support must be such that electrons are transmitted freely through it. The only substance that fulfils this requirement is a thin film of plastic material of a thickness of about 10^{-5} cm. and made from big molecules of such a size that they are just capable of forming continuous films. If any object is then placed upon such a film it will prevent to some extent the transmission of the beam of electrons through it

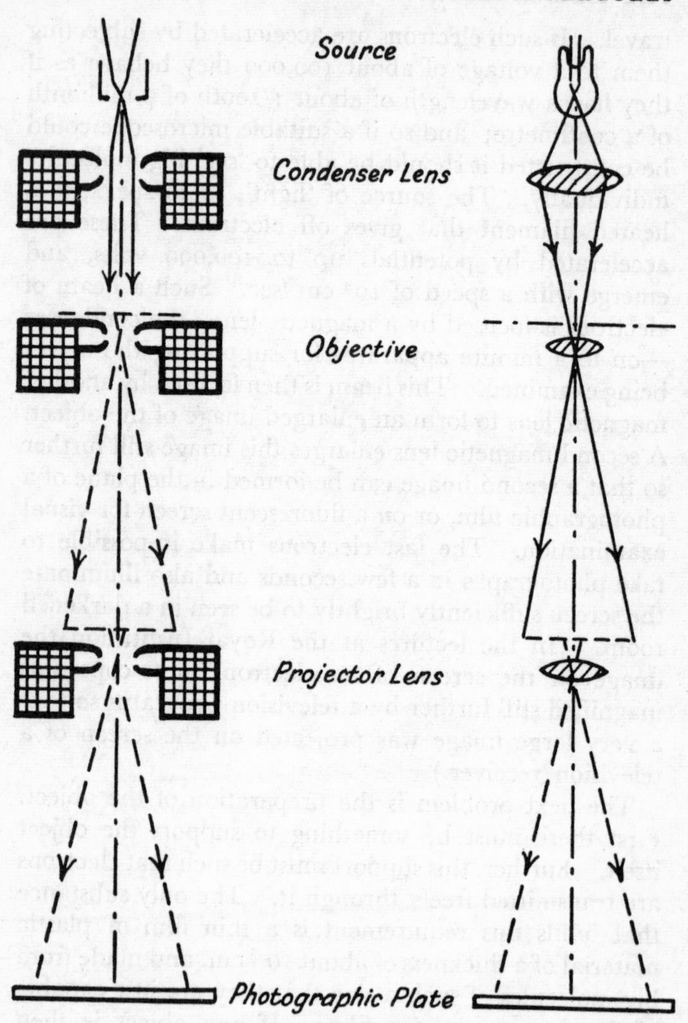

FIG. 2. Diagram to show the essential parts of the electron microscope (*left*) and an optical microscope (*right*). *Crown Copyright Reserved. National Physical Laboratory, Teddington, Mddx.*

and this will give rise to a shadow on the fluorescent screen. The method is thus based on shadows, except that the depth of the shadow depends on the thickness of the material deposited on the film. The problem then is to deposit individual molecules on the plastic film. The film itself will show irregularities because of the finite size of the molecules of which it is composed, and so the big molecules to be examined need to be a good deal bigger than those forming the film. The usual procedure is as follows. A very dilute solution of the substance to be examined is made, the concentration being about 0·001 per cent. by weight. To this solution there is added another liquid which precipitates the dissolved molecules. At first each particle of precipitate is an individual molecule, and if the suspension is dilute enough these individual molecules do not aggregate into larger clumps. A drop of this suspension is then allowed to fall on to a small disc spinning at 50,000 r.p.m. and driven by an air turbine. The drop is shattered into fine particles and a few of these are collected on the plastic film. These particles are so small that they have to be made 'visible' by giving them a coating of metallic gold or palladium. This is done by evaporating the metal on to the deposit at a very low angle so that each protuberance of a molecule casts a shadow on the film of plastic. This coating procedure has another important advantage, in that it protects the big molecules from being destroyed by the high energy electrons. With some types of big molecules electron bombardment causes their complete decomposition and the evaporation of the products.

Plate 1*b* shows an electron microscope picture of molecules of human hæmoglobin (from blood). It will be seen that all the molecules are spherical. This is because, even though the molecules are chain-like, on precipitation the chains coil up into a spherical structure. Thus no idea can be obtained about the shape of molecules from such pictures. Since the weight of a sphere is proportional to the cube of the radius, and since it is the radius that is measured in electron microscope photographs, the estimation of the weight of the molecule is not at all accurate. It is better to count the total number of molecules deposited from a known weight of material. The method is really one which demonstrates the discreteness or discontinuity of matter or the existence of molecules rather than one which is accurate at present for determining their size.

The Ultracentrifuge

Another method of measuring the size of very small particles consists in allowing them to settle in a liquid under the influence of gravity. Particles with a weight of 10^{-3} grams will settle in a few seconds and those with a weight of 10^{-5} grams in minutes; even particles with a weight of a millionth of a millionth of a gram will settle if one waits long enough. But this is still far larger than the size of big molecules. Even if one could devise an apparatus to observe the settling over a very small distance this would not solve the problem, because the continual bombardment of very fine particles by molecules in the surrounding liquid prevents completely the settling out of very small particles. The only alternative is to increase the force with which they settle out. This can be done by the use of a centrifuge—an ultracentrifuge in this case—as it is called. In order to get settling it is necessary to have a force of about 100,000 times that of gravity. This force is generated by rotating a disc say 6 inches in diameter at a speed of about 50,000 r.p.m. At such high speeds there is considerable force within the rotating disc, and it would certainly break if rotated at higher speeds. Fortunately it happens that high tensile steel and duralumin (an alloy of aluminium) are strong enough to permit the generation of centrifugal fields of a sufficient intensity to throw big molecules out of suspension in a matter of a few hours. A great deal of ingenuity has been displayed in overcoming the mechanical and optical difficulties involved in the construction of such a machine.

The rotor of the ultracentrifuge is a disc of steel or duralumin as shown in Plate 2*a*. Two holes in it contain two small cells also shown in Plate 2*a*. One of these holds the solution to be centrifuged and the other, the balancing cell, the solvent. This assembly must be supported and spun at high speed. In the original design of the machine the disc was suspended by a simple axle in a plain bearing and the drive was by compressed oil acting on a small turbine at the end of the axle. When spun at high speeds in air the rotor would become so hot that the sedimentation of the particles would be upset and it would not be possible to observe their movement accurately. It is therefore run in an enclosed space filled with hydrogen at low pressure for cooling. In another design the drive is by means of an air turbine, the rotor being suspended by a wire passing through a gland into the box in which the rotor is housed. In this case there is no bearing at all, and some of the air is used as a cushion to support the air turbine itself before being set into rotation. There is little friction in such a system and the rotor might take as long as half an hour to come to rest after a fast run. The air turbine has therefore a set of flutes or vanes machined into it arranged in opposite direction to the driving vanes so as to act as a brake when it is necessary to stop the rotation of the turbine. By suitable design it has proved possible to use an electric drive with the advantage of more precise control of the speed.

The next problem is to observe the speed at which the molecules are removed from the solution. This can only be done by optical methods. Usually the solutions are colourless and the only optical characteristic which varies with the concentration of the solution is the refractive index. The container for the solution in the rotor is fitted with suitable windows so that when the cells come opposite the windows in the box containing the rotor a photograph may be taken of the inside of the cell. What happens in practice is that as rotation proceeds there is a layer of pure solvent above the solution with a boundary between the two in which there is quite a sudden change of refractive

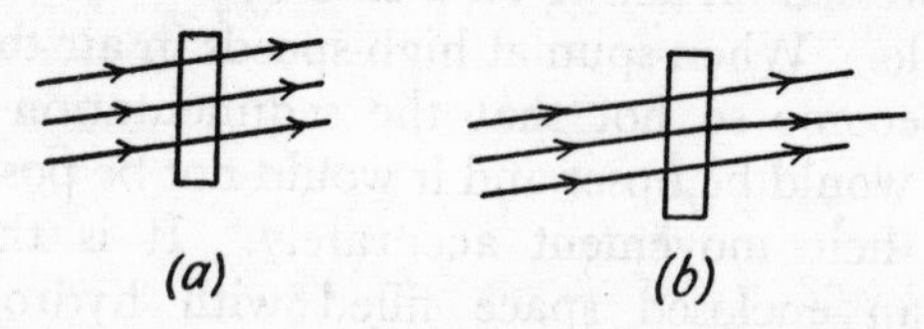

FIG. 3. *a* shows the path of a beam through a homogeneous liquid. *b* shows the path with the centre deflected owing to the change in refractive index.

index. If a beam of light is passed through a solution of uniform concentration it passes through without being deviated (fig. 3). If the same beam passes through a cell in which there is a solution at the bottom and pure solvent at the top, as happens in the centrifuge cell, then the first and third beams pass through unchanged in direction, but the second beam suffers a deflection on account of the sharp change in refractive index at the boundary. If therefore an observer were looking through such a cell at a geometrical pattern like a uniformly divided scale, then that scale will appear distorted at the position of the second beam. This is the same phenomenon as arises when looking at objects through a stream of hot air rising from a hot surface. As the rotation continues the boundary between the solvent and the solution moves downwards and so, by continuing the observation and noting when the distortion of the scale is at a maximum, the position of this boundary may be followed in time. There are more elaborate optical methods which display directly the change of refractive index of the boundary, so careful observation of scales is not really necessary.

In using the ultracentrifuge to measure sizes accurately, it is unfortunately necessary to know the shape of the molecule in solution. If it is spherical, then the velocity of sedimentation of the molecule can be used to calculate its size. On the other hand, if the molecule is rod-like, or is coiled up, then it is not possible to calculate the size, and supplementary experiments have to be carried out. There is, however, another ingenious way of doing the experiment. As the molecules move towards the bottom of the cell, there is set up a concentration gradient, so that molecules will tend to diffuse back and bring about uniform concentration in the solution. So there are two opposing forces—the centrifugal force tending to sediment the molecules out of solution, and the forces causing diffusion to establish uniformity of concentration.

If the centrifuge is run at a lower speed than for the complete sedimentation of the molecules it is possible to balance these two forces. Then by an examination, at balance, of the concentration of molecules in different parts of the cell, one can calculate the size of the molecules suspended in it.

Osmotic Pressure

The ultracentrifuge is an elaborate instrument and some of the calculations that must be done with the results are not at all easy, so other methods have had to be devised. One makes use of a very simple phenomenon. Suppose we set up three barometer tubes filled with mercury (fig. 4). The height of the mercury column is then a measure of the pressure of the atmosphere exerted on the surface of the mercury in the containing dish. Suppose next a small amount of ether is injected below the surface of the mercury so as to float on the surface of the mercury in the second tube, then the mercury level will be displaced, since some of the ether will evaporate and fill the evacuated space above the mercury. The difference in height between the two mercury levels is then a measure of the pressure of the vapour from the ether. Next a solid non-volatile acid (benzoic acid) is dissolved in

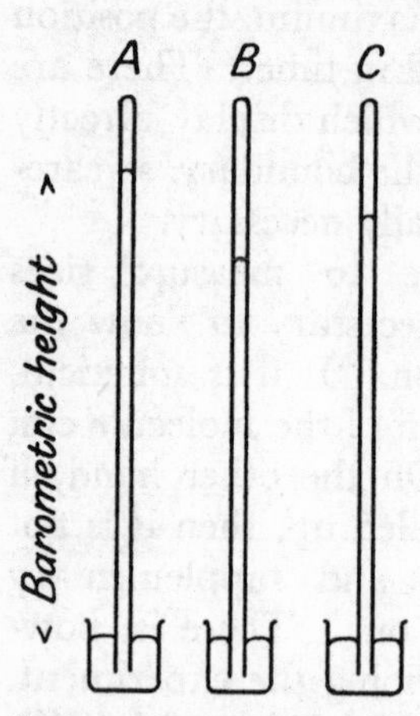

FIG. 4. Barometer tubes showing the vapour pressure of liquids and solutions.

ether and some of the solution injected into the third tube. Again the mercury level is depressed, but not so much as compared with the second tube. This means that the pressure of the vapour is diminished by dissolving in it an involatile material. In a way this is reasonable, because one can argue that the vapour pressure will have to do with the rate at which molecules of ether evaporate from the surface. So if some other molecule is present at the surface and cannot evaporate, fewer molecules of ether will evaporate and the vapour pressure will be correspondingly lowered. The important point about this phenomenon is that the reduction in vapour pressure depends only on the number of molecules per cubic centimetre of the liquid and not at all on their chemical nature, shape or size. So if we make a solution in which a known number of molecules is dissolved and measure the reduction in vapour pressure, a comparison with another solution in which the weight of dissolved material is known will enable one to calculate the number of the molecules in the second solution and therefore their individual weights. This procedure has been used by chemists for more than fifty years to measure weights of small molecules, because the effect is so large. For example, if we make a solution of 10 per cent. by weight of a small molecule, say a molecular weight of 100—a hydrogen atom being reckoned as unity—there would be a 10 per cent. reduction in vapour pressure. If the molecular weight were 1,000 for a 10 per cent. solution, the percentage reduction would only be 1; if 10,000, 0·1 per cent., and if 1,000,000, 0·001 per cent. Some of the big molecules normally met with in practice would cause such a minute reduction in vapour pressure that this direct method would be completely useless for this purpose. We have therefore to adopt another method to measure these differences accurately. It is based upon the following principles. Suppose again we start with a tube—a very tall tube this time, say 20,000 ft. high—and we put sufficient ether at the bottom so that when this ether has evaporated to fill the tube there is still some liquid remaining at the bottom. If now we measure the amount of ether in a cubic centimetre in different parts of the tube, we find that as we ascend it gets smaller and smaller, and at about 17,000 ft. it is only half what it is at the bottom of the tube. The reason for this decrease is simply that the gravitational pull of the earth gets smaller as one goes away from the centre. The same kind of phenomenon happens with the solution of the acid in the ether. Then if we set up the two tubes side by side with open ends, the ether concentration would be higher on the right side than on the left side, and if these tubes are connected, ether would diffuse from one side to the other and ultimately dissolve in the solution, so diluting it. In order to prevent this happening the left-hand tube would need to be raised so that the concentration at the tops of the tube was the same. The difference in liquid levels would then be a measure of the reduction of the vapour pressure. In order to find the position of liquid levels at which no transfer of vapour takes place it would be necessary to wait for very long periods, and the whole business would be completely impracticable. There is an alternative, however. If the two solutions are separated by a semi-permeable diaphragm such that the solvent can pass freely through the diaphragm and the dissolved molecules cannot do so, then transfer of the liquid can be brought about and a state of equilibrium reached much more quickly. This transfer of the liquid from the solvent to the solution is called osmosis. The advantage of this method is its extraordinary sensitivity. The 10 per cent. solution of acid would give rise to a difference in height of about 100 cm. Therefore, in the case of a big molecule, with a weight of 100,000, the difference would be about 1 mm. By the use of travelling microscopes it is possible to measure to 0·01 mm., so the possible error is about 1 per cent.

One of the biggest problems in using this method is to make such a semi-permeable membrane. This has got to be a structure that will act as a kind of molecular sieve, letting the little molecules of solvent through while preventing the passage of the large molecules dissolved in the solvent. Since the little molecules may have a diameter of only one hundredth of a millionth of an inch and the large ones one millionth of an inch, the holes must be exceedingly small. In spite of these severe requirements there are quite a number of materials which satisfy them. Various kinds of cellulose will work satisfactorily. For example, cellophane film before it is dried for normal use is a highly swollen jelly material; when the water is removed by repeated treatment with alcohol a network structure is formed which acts as such a semi-permeable membrane. Similarly fine powders such as nickel and some of the less fusible plastics can be fashioned into porous masses by heating and by pressure, using the process of partial fusing to decrease the pore size in these materials.

In designing the osmometer for these experiments various quite stringent conditions have also to be met. A typical large instrument is shown in Plate 2*b*. It consists of two very rigid slabs of brass. These are machined out to give a system of concentric rings interconnected. The two pieces are then bolted together, the diaphragm being clamped between the two faces. In this way a very large surface/volume ratio is obtained, so that only a very small volume of solvent need pass through the diaphragm in order to establish equilibrium. To each such cavity there is sealed a capillary tube so that the level of the liquids may be accurately compared. Similarly for filling and emptying the instrument there are suitably arranged valves.

Another most ingenious way of observing the transfer from solvent to solution consists in using a pair of thermojunctions as shown diagrammatically in figure 5,

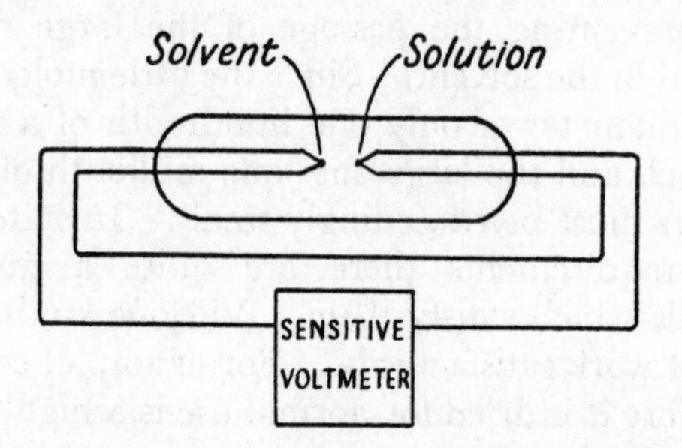

FIG. 5. Thermocouple method for measuring the difference in rates of evaporation from a pure liquid and a solution.

the two thermojunctions being suspended in a constant temperature enclosure. On one junction of the couple there is placed solvent and on the other solution. The system is then placed in a constant-temperature enclosure and allowed to come to temperature equilibrium. Solvent evaporates from the solution because of the high vapour pressure and condenses in the solution so the solvent is cooled by evaporation and the solution becomes hotter by condensation of solvent into it. This very slight temperature difference gives rise to a thermoelectric voltage which can be magnified and measured accurately by suitable devices. In this particular case the instrument is best calibrated by using solutions of known osmotic pressure so that the molecular weight of the dissolved substance can be accurately estimated.

Radioactive Methods

In the course of building big molecules it usually happens that the group of atoms at the end of the molecule is different from the arrangement in the repeating unit, which forms by weight the most important part. If the nature of this end structure is known and if there are methods which could measure the number of such terminal structures in a given weight of material, then the weight of each molecule would be simply equal to the weight of material divided by the number of end groups. With naturally occurring big molecules like rubber, the nature of the end groups is not known, but when big molecules are built up from small molecules synthetically, it is often possible to ensure that certain types of end group are incorporated in the molecule. For example, when an excess of acid reacts with an alcohol to form a long chain molecule there are two acid groups attached to each molecule. These acid groups can be titrated with alkali, so that the number in a given weight of material can be calculated. This method, however, becomes inaccurate when the number of units in the molecule exceeds about 100–200. At this point, however, the radioactive technique becomes of use. Ordinary carbon consists mostly of atoms of weight 12 (hydrogen 1 on the scale). There is also a small proportion of atoms of atomic weight 13. There is another kind of carbon with an atomic weight of 14 which is made in atomic piles. This carbon 14 is not stable—it is radioactive because it emits electrons and changes thereby into nitrogen 14. These electrons are emitted at considerable speeds and they can easily be counted by suitable equipment. If we start off with, say, 1,000 such radioactive atoms, 500 will have decomposed in 5,000 years, so there is plenty of time to do the whole experiment of making the molecule and examining it afterwards. The kinds of activity normally dealt with may give rise to 100 such atomic disintegrations per minute so we should need to start off with about $1 \cdot 6 \times 10^{10}$ atoms. These would only weigh 3×10^{-13} grams. Since radioactive detection instruments record the disintegration of a single atom, the method is extraordinarily sensitive for detecting small amounts of matter, millions of times smaller than can be dealt with by any known chemical manipulation. It is not necessary even to activate all the atoms. The method is ideal for use with big molecules because there may be as few as 1 end group per 10,000 units for a molecular weight of about 1,000,000 and a precision of 1 per cent. in the measurements is desirable. On p. 26 it was shown how the fragment of a molecule would induce small molecules to grow into larger ones in such a way that the molecular fragment is incorporated at the end of the molecule. In order to carry out the experiment a known weight of initiating molecules, partly made of radioactive carbon, is oxidised so that all the carbon is converted into carbon dioxide. This gas is then

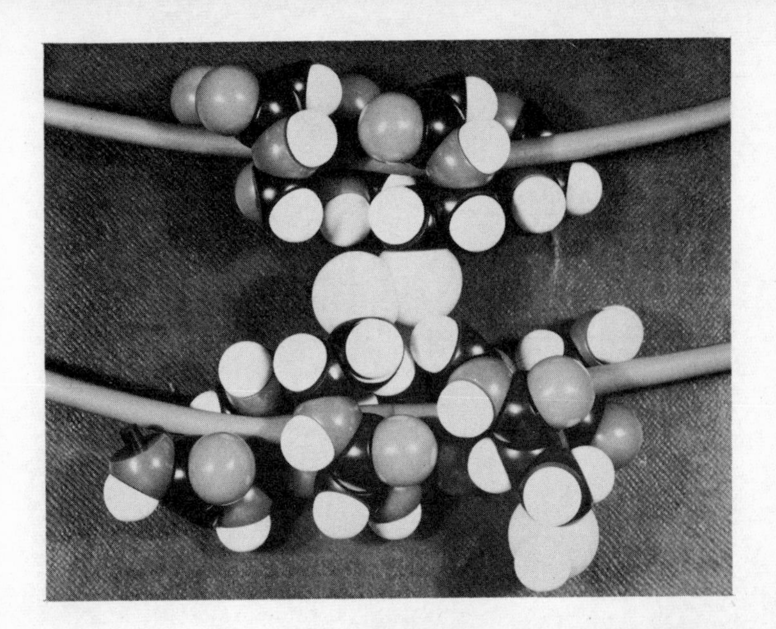

1*a*. Models of the structure of hair showing the sulphur atoms (large white balls) linking the long chains together. (See p. 40.)

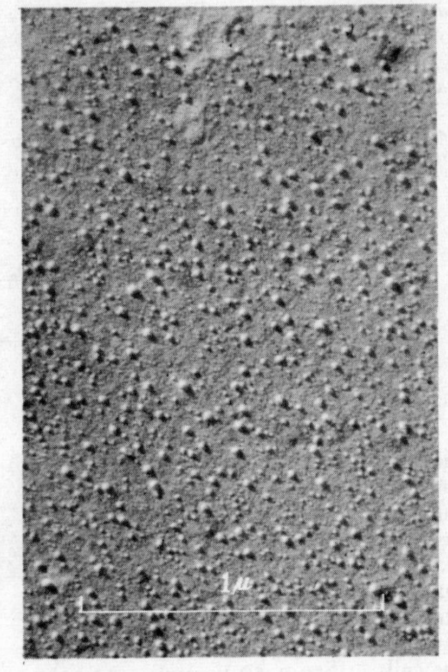

1*b*. Electron microscope photograph of individual molecules of haemoglobin from human blood. (1μ is $\frac{1}{1000}$ mm.) (See p. 51.)

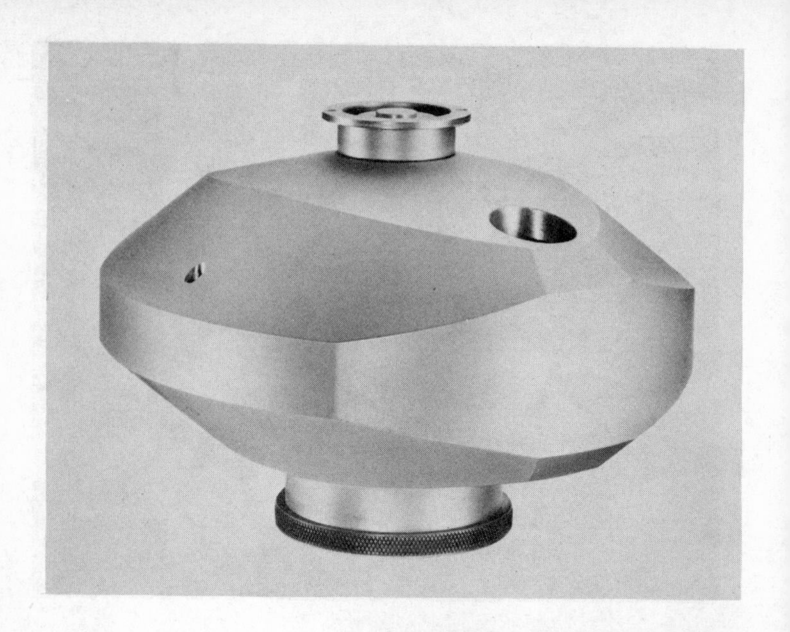

2*a*. Ultracentrifuge—cells and rotor. (See p. 53.)

Photograph by courtesy of Dr. Edward G. Pickels from 'Methods of Medical Research, Vol. 5' (Year Book Publishers, Chicago, Ill. U.S.A.).

2*b*. Osmometer. This is normally immersed in a temperature controlled water bath. The inner two vertical glass tubes are examined by means of a travelling microscope. The outer tubes are used for filling and the knobs at the bottom are the control valves for emptying the cells. (See p. 59.)

admitted to an apparatus called a Geiger counter (after the name of the inventor). This is simply a glass tube containing a copper cylinder and an insulated fine wire down the axis of the tube. When a voltage of about 1,500 is applied to the wire and the pressure of gas is suitably adjusted, the tube behaves in a rather peculiar, but useful way. If a carbon atom in a CO_2 molecule disintegrates, a fast-moving electron will be shot through the gas. This knocks more electrons off neighbouring molecules, giving rise to many positive ions. Because of the high electric potential applied to the electrodes of the tube, the positive ions and the electrons are separately and rapidly removed. In this way an amplification of the original event is made and the small pulse of current that passes can further be amplified by electronic valves to produce a pulse big enough to operate counting devices. The data so provided give the number of counts per gram of material. Next, the big molecule is made by the methods described in Chapter 1 and a given weight oxidised and counted as before. There will, of course, be a big reduction in the number of counts, but the ratio of the two counts gives a measure of the number of end groups per molecule, and therefore of the size of the molecule itself.

The above process depends on putting the radioactive atom at the end of the molecule, but it is possible to conduct the experiment in another way. By suitable means a bromine atom, for example, can be located at the end of a molecule. By neutron bombardment in an atomic pile it can be rendered very strongly radioactive, and its activity can readily be measured without the necessity of having to oxidise, and therefore destroy, the specimen.

A most striking and visible demonstration of these so-called end-group methods can be done with woven nylon fabric. At the end of the nylon molecule there is a group NH_2, which is really part of the ammonia molecule NH_3. It acts as a base, just as does ammonia. Nylon fibres can be dyed readily with dyestuffs which contain acid groups; these groups react with the basic groups in the nylon; and the dye molecule is therefore anchored to the end of the nylon molecule. For a given weight of fibre there will be a diminishing number of basic groups and therefore less tendency to dye as the size of the molecule increases. So, if a relative estimate is to be made of the size of the nylon molecules, it can be obtained by immersing the fibre or cloth woven from it, in a suitable dye-bath and comparing the depth of dyeing by suitable devices.

The Method of Light Scattering

A further completely different principle may be used in yet another method for the determination of size. It might well be asked why so many methods should be needed simply to measure one quantity relating to big molecules. The answer is that not one of these methods can be used with the complete range of molecular sizes which is dealt with in practice. Sometimes special solvents have to be used at high temperatures, and only some of the methods are usable under such conditions. In addition, it is important to find another method based upon very different principles to see whether similar results are obtained as compared with the other methods. The light-scattering method is based on a well-known optical phenomenon. If a beam of light is passed through an absolutely dust-free liquid, the path of the beam can always be seen by the amount of light scattered by the liquid. The reason for this scattering is simply that the rapid motion of the molecules change the refractive index of the medium in any particular small element of volume. If the liquid is made into a plastic solid, as can be done by the methods described in Chapter 1, the amount of scattered light is significantly cut down because the molecules are then frozen into position. In the same way if big molecules are dissolved in the solvent, the latter being chosen so that the solution had a different refractive index from that of the pure solvent, the motion of the big molecules produces changes in the refractive index and additional scattering occurs. This is quite different from what occurs when the molecules are precipitated out of solution, when the system becomes quite turbid on account of the light scattered at the boundary between the spherical particle and the suspending medium. By measuring accurately the intensity of the incident and scattered light and also measuring the refractive index of the solution, optical theory permits the calculation of the weight of the particle that scatters the light. The formula relating these quantities is a very complicated one, but the calculations are similar to those made a long time ago when the theory of the blue colour of the sky was developed. Not only do transparent liquids scatter light, so also do gases, but to a much smaller degree—in fact the scattering can only be appreciated on a relatively large scale. The sky appears blue because the blue light from the sun is scattered 16 times more intensely than the red light. Again, if the ratio of the intensity of the scattered to the incident light is known, it is possible to calculate the weights of the

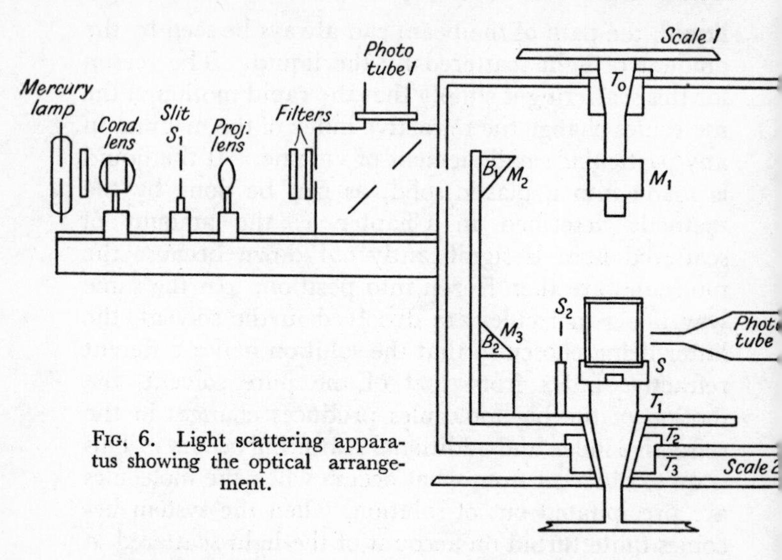

FIG. 6. Light scattering apparatus showing the optical arrangement.

molecules of the oxygen and nitrogen comprising the atmosphere.

The kinds of instruments that have been developed for making these measurements depend on modern developments of photoelectric devices. The fraction of the light scattered may be as little as one hundred thousandth of that of the incident light, and that small fraction must be measured with an accuracy of at least 1 per cent. In a darkened room the scattered light is just visible to the naked eye, so it needs rather special photoelectric cells to measure it accurately. In order to measure the small photoelectric current produced, a device called a photomultiplier is used. First of all there is a photosensitive surface made mainly of cæsium, which is a metal like sodium. This emits a few electrons when illuminated, but these are too few to measure accurately. The electrons are attracted inside the photoelectric device to a positively charged plate the surface of which is coated with a special composition, so that if one electron collides with the surface two or more electrons are given off. It is possible to put as many as 14 stages of acceleration into the tube so that the initial low current may be magnified a million times or more and can easily be measured on robust instruments like milliammeters. A diagram of the instrument is shown in figure 6. First there is a point source of light—an arc between tungsten rods in mercury vapour. By means of lenses and slits the light is made into an accurately defined parallel beam. Before this beam is projected into the instrument itself, a small fraction of it is transmitted by a semi-transparent mirror into a photomultiplier tube so that a continuous record may be kept of the intensity of the arc lamp. The beam then strikes a mirror, M_1, capable of rotation, then on to another mirror, M_2, and finally a third mirror, M_3, so that it can be projected into a glass cell containing the solution to be examined. Another photomultiplier cell picks up the scattered light through a system of circular diaphragms and the current is accurately measured. The intensity of light in the incident beam is measured by replacing the cell by a piece of practically perfectly white reflecting material—magnesium carbonate—and measuring in the same way the intensity of the light scattered. The ratio of these two currents can then be used to calculate the weight of the big molecules in solution.

This highly precise instrument can also be used for measuring the dimensions of big molecules in solution. The elaborate system of mirrors described above, permits the beam to be directed into the solution from a large number of angles, so that the intensity of the scattered light may be investigated as the angle of incidence is varied. These results may be represented by a suitable diagram (fig. 7). Suppose O is the point in the solution which is observed by the photoelectric cell, and the light travels from left to right in the

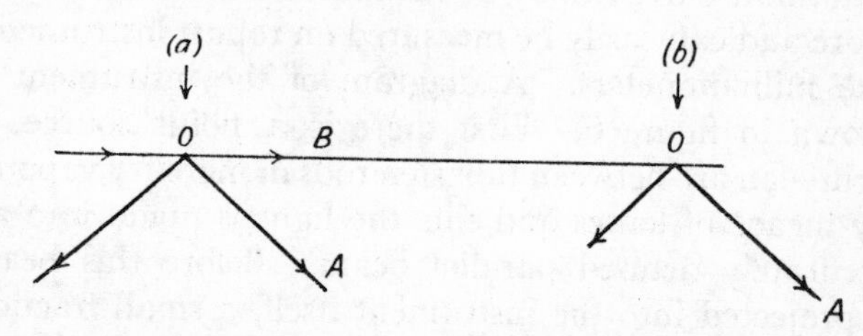

FIG. 7. *a* shows that the intensity of the light scattered in the forward and backward directions is the same. *b* shows that the intensity scattered in the backward direction is diminished compared with that in the forward direction.

direction OB. Suppose, next, the photocell observes in the direction OA, making an angle AOB with the incident beam. The intensity of the beam of light may be represented by the length of the line OA. In this way another diagram may be constructed in which the length of the line OA to the edge of the diagram at any point gives a measure of the intensity of light scattered in that direction. Normally this is a symmetrical figure along the direction OA and also at right angles to it. When a solution of big molecules is examined, the curve changes its shape very markedly. Under comparable conditions the intensity of light scattered in the forward direction is the same as before, but there is much less light scattered backwards. This happens because the length of the big molecule is comparable with the wavelength of visible light. For example, green light has a wavelength of 5×10^{-5} cm.

The molecules normally dealt with have, even in the coiled-up position, a length quite comparable with this wavelength. By measuring accurately the ratio of the intensities of the light scattered at say 45° and 135° to the incident beam, it is possible to calculate the distance between the ends of the molecule. The results of this type of measurement are very surprising. Suppose we measure the weight of such a big molecule of polyethylene $(C_2H_4)_n$ by the methods described above, and it comes out at 560,000. Now if this molecule were stretched out so that all the carbon atoms in the backbone were in the same plane, then it is possible to calculate the length of the molecule, since the distance between the centres of the atoms is $1{\cdot}54 \times 10^{-8}$ cm. and the angle between the bonds between the carbon atoms is 109° and each unit weighs on the hydrogen atom scale 28. There will thus be 20,000 units in the structure, and thus the length of the molecule is 5×10^{-4} cm. In solution, however, the molecule is much shorter at 5×10^{-5} cm. This means that it is coiled up to a very considerable extent. There is no special difficulty about a molecule doing this, because the units are joined together by single links or bonds between the carbon atoms. Further, it is possible to rotate one unit with respect to the neighbouring unit without difficulty. The effect is to give a much more compact structure. This coiling up is in fact a natural configuration for the molecules to attain. The degree to which coiling up occurs depends on the nature of the solvent. The better the solvent, that is the more it interacts physically with the big molecule, the more will the big molecule be stretched out. As solvent power is decreased, for example by adding another liquid which is not a solvent for the big molecule, so the molecule coils up until in the limit when it is precipitated out of solution it has in fact coiled up into a spherical shape as confirmed by the electron microscope picture in Plate 1*b*. This ability of a molecule to coil and uncoil more or less easily is a phenomenon of the utmost importance in the behaviour of substances composed of large molecules. In fact the skill in making big molecules to serve defined purposes is based upon an exact knowledge of the factors that govern the shape of a molecule in a specified environment. In the following chapter some of the consequences of these matters will be dealt with in greater detail.

Viscosity

One of the most striking characteristics of solutions of big molecules is their thickness or high viscosity. If a solution is passed down a tube it flows much more slowly than the solvent itself. Even solutions containing a few per cent. of material may be a thousand times thicker than the solvent itself. If the concentration is made greater the whole solution may in fact set into a rigid jelly. In other words, the presence of big molecules can immobilise the liquid in which they are dissolved. This again is simply another phenomenon connected with the bigness of molecules. These thickening effects depend on size, and for a given concentration the thickness or viscosity increases with increasing molecular size. In fact by measuring the viscosity of a solution it is possible to obtain an approximate idea of the size of the dissolved molecules, but the method is not an absolute one, as are the other methods previously described. The big molecules are extended, and therefore in quite weak solution they tend to make contact with each other, linking together to give a rigidity to the whole solution. Besides this the solvent molecules (especially if it is a good solvent) have a tendency to cling to the big molecules, so in a way part of the solvent is not so mobile as it would be in the pure state. If a force is applied to move such a liquid the combined interlocking of the big molecules and the interaction with the solvent makes the whole business more difficult, and thus the thickness or viscosity is markedly increased. The larger the molecule the greater the interlocking will be and hence the greater the viscosity.

There is another interesting phenomenon associated with such solutions. If the solution is allowed to flow through a tube, then there is a tendency for the molecules to line up in the direction of flow. The result is that the interlocking between molecules is cut down and in some cases this entices the liquid to flow rather more easily. Up to a limit, then, the quicker the liquid is pushed through, the easier it is to do the job. When the liquid becomes stationary again the molecules interlock and the original state of affairs is attained. This kind of effect is important in all sorts of practical applications.

For instance it is important that when paint is applied by a brush or spray, the process of application should be easy, the liquid flow readily and brush-marks disappear quickly. It is equally important that once the paint is applied it should not only stick to the surface but also it should not run off a vertical surface. So it is necessary to have a medium that will thicken up rapidly again after it has been worked by a brush or similar device.

The apparatus for determining the thickness of a

liquid is shown in figure 8. The name given to the instrument is a viscometer. The first kind is simply a U-tube, one limb being wide and the other narrow, 0·5–1 mm. in diameter. There is a bulb at the top of the narrow tube and two marks in the tube to define a volume of liquid. The solvent is sucked up into this bulb above the top registration mark, and then allowed to flow. The time taken for the liquid level to pass from the top to the bottom marks is noted. The solution is similarly run through the viscometer. The ratio of times of flow then gives very nearly the numerical value of the ratio of the viscosities of the

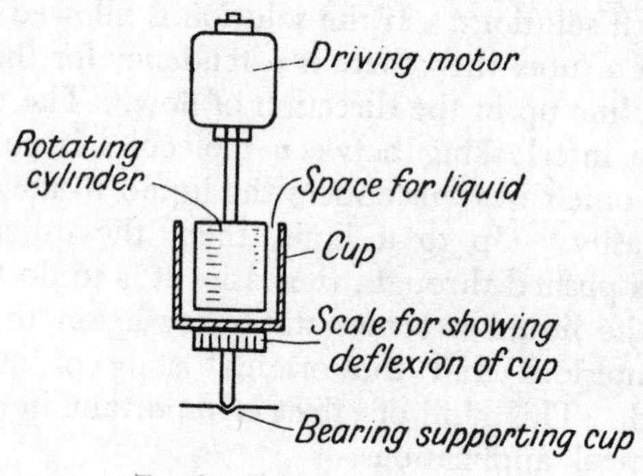

FIG. 8. Cylinder viscometer.

solution and of the solvent. The other type is more complicated in construction, but is of more use in finding out how the solution behaves at different rates of flow. The liquid to be investigated is contained in a cup. This is held vertically in a suitable bearing and is restrained by a spring concentric with the axis of the cup. A pointer and scale is attached to measure the angular deflection of the cup when the experiment is in progress. Inside the cup there is a cylinder (or rotor) which can be rotated at a controlled speed by an electric motor. When the rotor is moving at a fixed speed it transmits motion to the liquid, which in turn rotates the cup, this rotation being opposed by the spring. An equilibrium position for the cup is thus attained, and this is a measure of the viscosity of the liquid. By altering the speed of the motor it is possible to determine how the viscosity is affected by the energy transmitted to the liquid by the rotor.

Network Systems

It has already been mentioned that it is possible to build up molecular networks in which the long chains of atoms are linked together into a three-dimensional network. Since there is no limit to the number of chains so linked, the size of the molecule cannot really be defined—in fact it is as big as the piece of material being examined. The physical properties of the substance are then determined, not only by the chemical nature of the backbone, but also to a very marked extent by the frequency of the links between the chains. So to complete the methods for the general examination of big molecules it is necessary to have a method of determining how many cross links there are per 100 units in the big molecule. This can be done by making use of the ideas about the behaviour of big molecules. Suppose we consider a small spherical piece of cross-linked material. In this condition the molecular chains are coiled up as they are in a precipitated linear big molecule. When the sphere is brought into contact with a liquid, which is a solvent for the linear molecule, these chains will take up solvent and begin to stretch out. The result is that the sphere swells uniformly in all directions. But this expansion does not go on indefinitely, since the cross links put a limit to the extension of the molecular chains. Thus the sphere expands to a defined size, and of course it can never dissolve in the liquid. The greater the number of cross links, the less easy it is for the sphere to swell. The theory of this effect has been worked out and a relationship derived which connects the amount of swelling with the frequency of cross linking for a given solvent-solid system. Plate *3a* shows the extent to which swelling occurs for varying frequencies of cross-linking.

CHAPTER

* 3 *

FIBRES

All fibres, whether natural or artificial, consist of large molecules. In fact the existence of large molecules makes it possible to produce fine cylinders of material that have very high strength while possessing the necessary flexibility needed for their manufacture into woven fabrics. The first job is to convert the long molecules into fine filaments. There are three general methods of carrying out this operation. Some of the materials, such as nylon and Terylene, melt at temperatures approaching 300° C. to form viscous liquids. Such a liquid may be forced through fine holes so that the filament emerges as a column of molten material which soon solidifies. This is the process of melt-spinning. The second general method consists in dissolving the material in a suitable solvent and pumping the solution through a fine orifice. There are two variants of this method. If the solvent is easily volatile it may be removed simply by allowing it to evaporate in a stream of hot air. Alternatively the solvent may be removed by allowing it to dissolve in a suitable liquid. The first is the dry-spinning method and the second the wet-spinning method. The process to be adopted depends on the nature of the filament because some molecules such as cellulose do not melt and need to be spun from a solvent—others, like Terylene, melt but do not easily dissolve in any solvent at moderate temperatures.

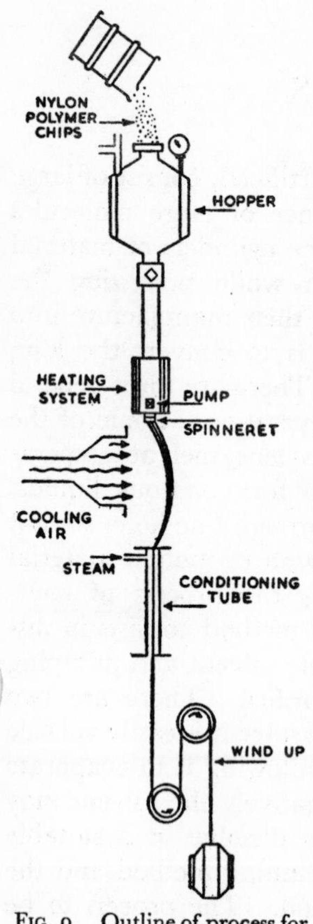

FIG. 9. Outline of process for spinning nylon.

Melt Spinning

Typical of melt spinning operations is that employed in the manufacture of nylon. The general outline of the process is shown in figure 9. Nylon in the form of small chips 1/8–1/4 in. in size is loaded into a hopper. In turn this hopper feeds a pot in which the melting occurs in an inert atmosphere such as nitrogen or steam to prevent oxidation of the nylon. When molten the nylon is pumped through the system of fine holes in the spinneret (it would be uneconomic to have simply one hole in the device). Cooling air soon solidifies the filament, which then passes through a conditioner, where it spends a short time in an atmosphere of steam. It is then given a coating of size for subsequent processing and is finally wound up on to

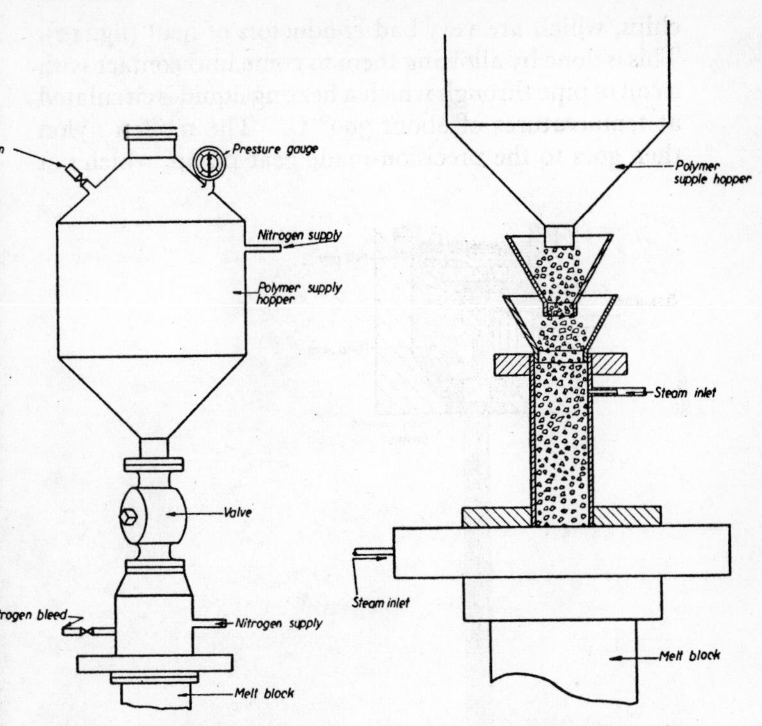

FIG. 10. Arrangement for melting nylon in the presence of nitrogen.

FIG. 11. Arrangement for melting nylon in the presence of steam.

Reproduced from R. Hill: 'Fibres from Synthetic Polymers'. (Elsevier Publishing Company, Amsterdam, 1953.)

a bobbin. The details of this complex process are shown in figures 10 and 11, where the different arrangements for keeping an atmosphere of nitrogen round the hot chips are shown. If such a blanket were not used the nylon would oxidise and become less easy to melt, making it quite impossible to produce a satisfactory filament. The next problem is to impart heat to the chips, which are very bad conductors of heat (fig. 12). This is done by allowing them to come into contact with a coil of pipe through which a heating liquid is circulated at temperatures of about 300° C. The molten nylon then goes to the precision-made gear pump, which not

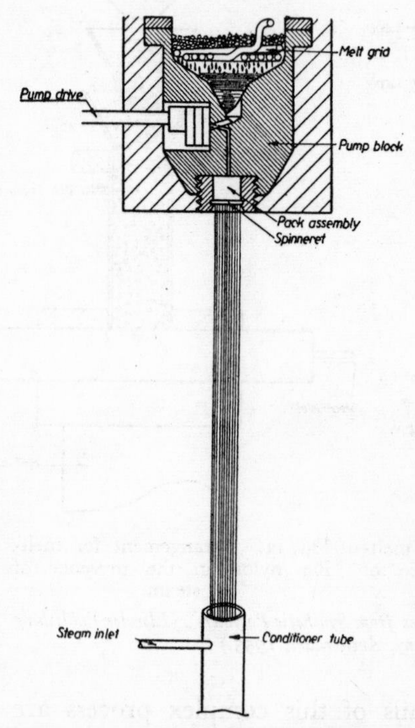

FIG. 12. Details of the melting and pumping of nylon. *Reproduced from R. Hill: 'Fibres from Synthetic Polymers'. (Elsevier Publishing Company, Amsterdam, 1953.)*

only acts as a pump, at a pressure of about 1000 lb./sq. in., but also acts as a metering device to control the supply of nylon to the holes of the spinneret. Before actual spinning the molten material is filtered through a pack of sand which removes any non-molten chip or other

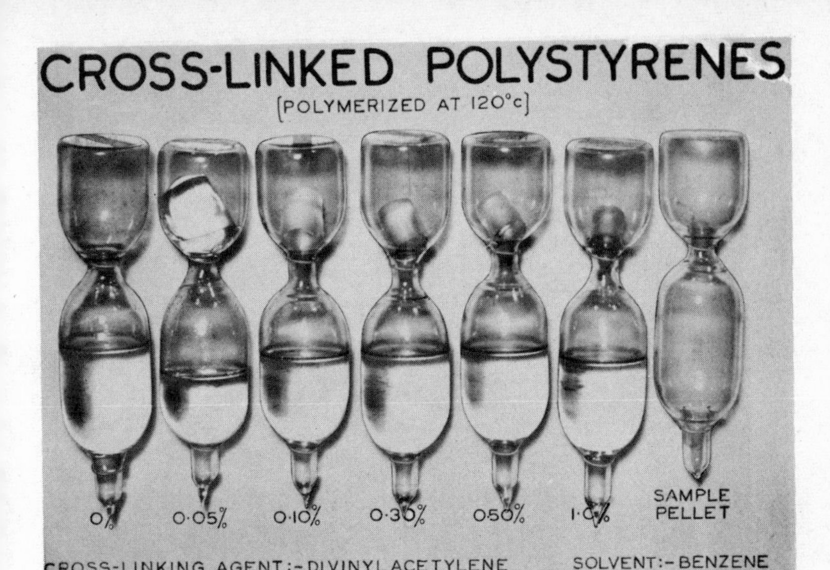

3*a*. Swelling of cross-linked systems with the different amounts of cross linking. (1 per cent. cross-linking agent gives approximately 1 link per 100 units.) (See p. 74.) *Courtesy of Prof. Norrish.*

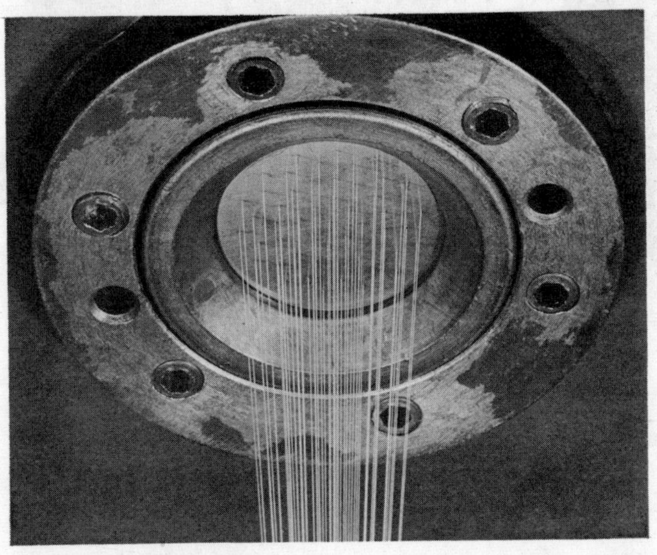

3*b*. Molten nylon filaments emerging from the holes in the spinneret. (See p. 79.)

4. Filaments emerging from the spinneret. (See p. 81.)
Photograph by courtesy of Union Carbide Chemicals Company, New York.

extraneous matter that might spoil the quality of the filament. The spinneret itself is a flat disc of steel about 1/4 in. thick and 2–3 in. in diameter, perforated with a large number of holes so as to give an even supply of molten nylon to each hole. Sometimes the orifice is made in the form of a slot in order to make

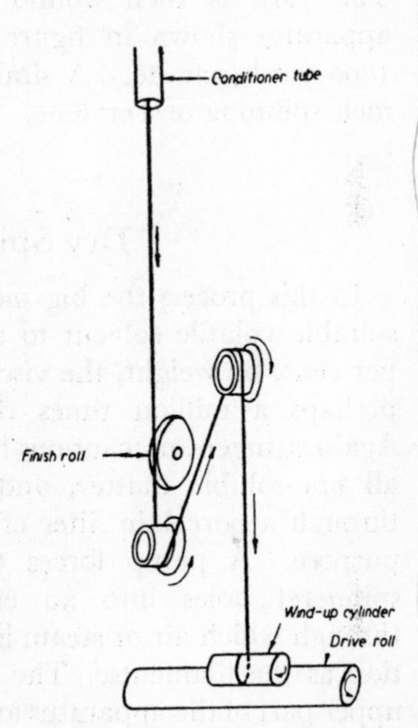

FIG. 13. Winding up the nylon filaments. *Reproduced from R. Hill: 'Fibres from Synthetic Polymers'. (Elsevier Publishing Company, Amsterdam, 1953.)*

non-circular filaments for special effects. Plate 3*b* shows the filament emerging from the face of the spinneret. The filaments solidify about 2 ft. below the face of the spinneret when the temperature reaches 260° C. At this time the diameter of the filament is appreciably less than that of the holes through which it has come. The yarn so produced is free from moisture and it is essential to rehumidify it in steam so that it is in equilibrium with the moisture in the atmosphere. If this were not done the yarn would change its length and cause trouble in the winding on to bobbins. More water and lubricant are added by running the yarn against a roller immersed in liquid. The yarn is then wound on to a bobbin by the apparatus shown in figure 13 at a speed of nearly 1000 yards/minute. A similar process is used for the melt spinning of Terylene.

Dry Spinning

In this process the big molecules are dissolved in a suitable volatile solvent to a concentration of several per cent. by weight, the viscosity of the solution being perhaps a million times that of the solvent itself. Again stringent precautions have to be taken to remove all non-soluble matter, and the solution is pumped through a porcelain filter of cylindrical shape for this purpose. A pump forces the solution through the spinneret holes into an enclosed heated chamber through which air or steam is blown in the same direction as the filaments. The solvent evaporates in the upper part of the apparatus and the multi-filament yarn is withdrawn at the bottom and wound up without any further treatment. The speeds and volume of air required depend on the nature of the fibre and its diameter. One of the vital economic factors is the recovery of the expensive solvent used in the process. In the spinning of cellulose acetate, in which acetone is used, the most elaborate methods are employed to remove the solvent from the air stream after it has gone through the spinning apparatus. This may be done by dissolving it in water or by absorbing the acetone on solid carbon. In both cases it is possible to recover more than 95 per cent. of the solvent, which is used over and over again. For the thicker yarns spinning may actually be done upwards, since this prevents undue pull on the newly formed filament, as would happen in the downward method of spinning. A photograph of the spinneret face and part of the enclosed spinning tube is shown in Plate 4. In order to evaporate the solvent quickly these cells are kept at temperatures of about 100° C., and in the case of cellulose acetate the spinning solution is at 50° C., so that extremely rapid evaporation of the solvent takes place, permitting wind-up speeds of the yarn of the order of 100 yd./minute or more.

Wet Spinning

In this process the solution is passed through the spinneret into a bath which removes the solvent and precipitates the big molecules in the form of a fibre. By far the most important process here is the production of so-called viscose yarns from cellulose from a variety of sources. This type of rayon is made and used in quantities comparable to that of cotton. Since its introduction many years ago it has been improved in quality, and for sheer tonnage it is the most important of man-made fibres. Here the problem is to get an effective and cheap solvent for the cellulose. This is done by steeping the cellulose in strong caustic-soda solution. In this respect cellulose has a structure like an alcohol, and may be written ROH for the present purpose. The reaction with caustic soda may then be written:

$$ROH + NaOH = RONa + H_2O$$

This soda cellulose has the valuable property of dissolving in a liquid called carbon disulphide, which has a formula similar to carbon dioxide, except that the oxygen atoms are replaced by sulphur atoms, so that its formula is CS_2. A clear golden-coloured solution is formed, which is allowed to stand for some time, during which period changes in the size of the cellulose molecule occur and make the solution more suitable for spinning. Again the liquid is carefully filtered and pumped through a spinneret immersed in a bath of dilute sulphuric acid. On extruding the filament into such a bath precipitation at once occurs, first into a soft jelly-like filament of little strength (Plate 6*a*). The simple chemistry of the process is probably that the caustic soda is neutralised by the sulphuric acid to form sodium sulphate and water. This releases the carbon disulphide, which evaporates, and simultaneously the cellulose is precipitated. During this process the sodium sulphate is formed within the fibre, so it has to undergo a most thorough washing to remove sulphate and sulphuric acid. During this process the fibre diminishes

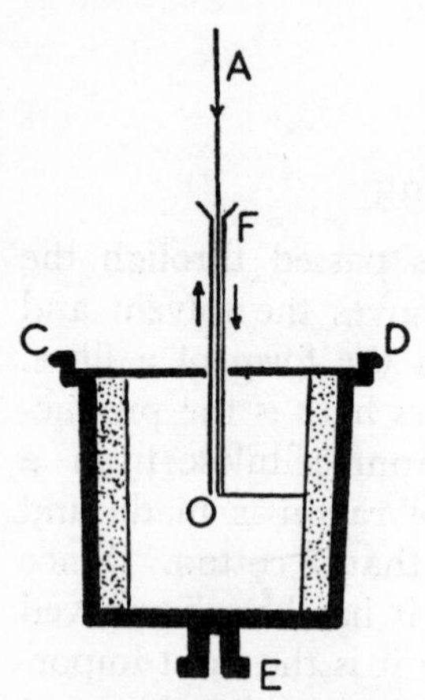

FIG. 14. Topham box for the collection of spun filaments. *Reproduced from R. Hill: 'Fibres from Synthetic Polymers'. (Elsevier Publishing Company, Amsterdam, 1953.)*

in size. The collection of the wet yarn on to a bobbin is a more difficult operation than in dry spinning. It is achieved in practice by a Topham box, which is illustrated in figure 14. This consists of a hollow cylinder CED made of aluminium or plastic and rotated at about 6,000 r.p.m. The yarn in A is fed through the funnel, FO. On touching the pot, fibre is centrifuged to the side. The funnel can be raised and lowered so that the yarn is deposited as a cylinder on the side of the pot. The sides of the pot diverge slightly so that the resultant cake may easily be removed for further processing.

Crystallisation Phenomena in Fibres

The formation of the yarn is only the first step in the manufacture of a man-made fibre. Many operations have to be done before the filament is ready for weaving into cloth. There is an important behaviour exhibited by big molecules, especially of the nylon, Terylene and polyethylene types. If a solid is allowed to cool from temperatures just below its melting point down to room temperature and a record is kept of the drop in temperature during the process, the record is a perfectly smooth one, that is to say the temperature gradually decreases as the time increases. The effect is different with a variety of nylon, for example, called 610, which melts at 215° C., a rather lower temperature than ordinary nylon. If one follows the decrease in temperature as a plug of the solid cools, then at about 206° C. the temperature remains constant for a few minutes (fig. 15). This is exactly similar to what happens when a cooling curve is plotted for a liquid that crystallises at a definite temperature (fig. 16). Here the temperature

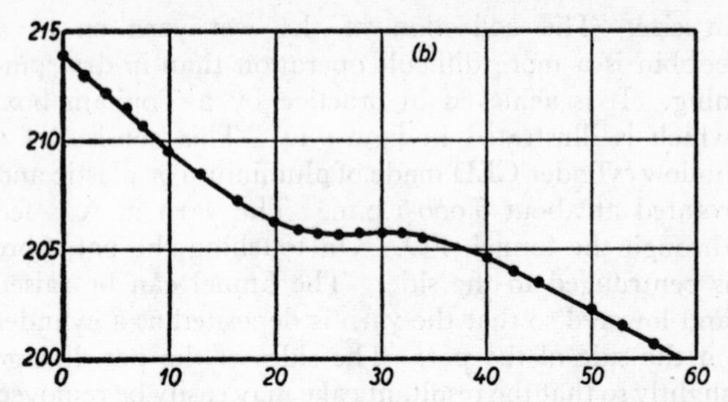

FIG. 15. Cooling curve for solid nylon 610. *Reproduced from R. Hill: 'Fibres from Synthetic Polymers'. (Elsevier Publishing Company, Amsterdam, 1953.)*

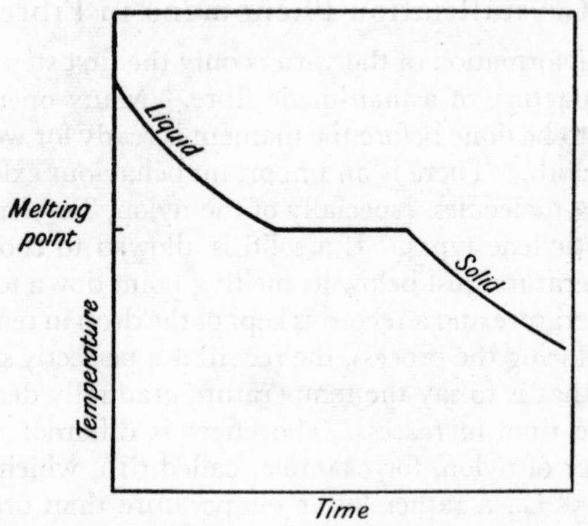

FIG. 16. Cooling curve for a typical pure liquid–solid system.

remains constant for a certain time at the melting point, while the liquid mass solidifies and the latent heat of fusion is evolved. In the cooling of nylon 610 the heat must be produced at 206° C. during the period

25–30 minutes. Hence we must conclude that in spite of the fact that the nylon is really solid, crystallisation must be occurring during this period. In the molten nylon the molecules are oriented in all possible directions, twisting and turning and changing their shape and positions continually. When the temperature falls to 215° C., the molecules become frozen into position more or less in the orientation which they had in the molten liquid just before solidification occurred. In the solid state there is no particular orientation of the molecules. At such a high temperature, although the nylon is solid the individual molecules have some small freedom of movement, and these molecules have a tendency to attract each other, and in particular they tend to line up so that the backbones are parallel to each other over considerable distances. This parallel orientation of the chains gives rise to a regular pattern of atoms similar to that which occurs in a crystal. In this case no crystal faces are produced. The little crystalline regions are themselves oriented in all directions. It may happen that one long molecule may go through two or more crystalline regions. So the crystals have fringes which make it impossible for the substance to show definite crystal faces. If these substances are examined by an optical or an electron microscope, regions of orientation can be located as definite geometrical patterns. These phenomena are not shown by big molecular weight substances, which fail to form satisfactory and strong fibres; hence one of the essential features of fibre-forming substances is that the molecules must be capable of fitting together into a precise geometrical pattern so as to form small crystals in the solid.

Cold Drawing

Crystallisation is not in itself sufficient. This is perhaps best illustrated by referring to nylon. If a nylon filament is pulled with quite a small force it yields readily, exhibiting no great strength. Such stretching may be continued without exerting a greater force until the fibre is about four times as long as it was originally and then, quite suddenly, it becomes much more difficult to draw, and in fact if a greater force is applied the fibre extends only to a limited extent and ultimately will break. This is the phenomenon of cold drawing. As a matter of fact these fibres may also be drawn at high temperatures too. In the cold-drawing process there is another curious phenomenon. The diameter of the whole fibre does not decrease uniformly during the stretching; instead the first pull on the fibre produces a neck, that is a region where there is a comparatively quick change in diameter of the fibre. As stretching progresses it would appear as if the neck moves to the left as the filament is pulled out of the undrawn yarn to the right. This cold drawing enormously increases the strength of the fibre. Photographs of the drawn and undrawn parts are shown in Plate 5. The second photograph is taken with what is known as a polarising microscope, which gives an indication of the way in which the crystals are oriented in a crystalline body. In the undrawn part the fibre is illuminated in such a way as to indicate not only crystallinity but also random orientation of the crystals themselves. In the drawn part the appearance of the photograph shows that orientation of the crystallites has taken place. By using X- and infra-red rays, it is possible to learn about the orientation of the molecules within the drawn fibre, and these methods confirm the idea that the molecules are lying parallel to the axis of

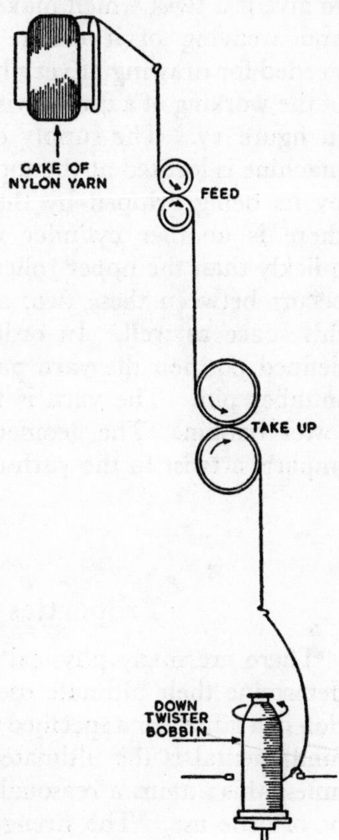

FIG. 17. The draw-twisting of nylon showing the outline of the process.

the fibre. It is this orientation brought about by stretching that gives strength to the fibres. The molecular chains are still sufficiently flexible to bend and allow the fabric to drape in the way that is necessary.

After the spinning operation the yarn has therefore to be subjected to a stretching operation as it is wound from one bobbin to another. In addition, it is desirable to give it a twist which makes the subsequent handling and weaving of it easier. Elaborate machinery is needed for drawing at very high speeds, and an outline of the working of a draw-twister, as it is called, is shown in figure 17. The supply of yarn from the spinning machine is located at the top and the yarn is unwound by its being gripped by the two rollers. Below this there is another cylinder rotating four times more quickly than the upper roller. The drawing therefore occurs between these two, and the neck is located in this space as well. In order to keep the neck in a defined position the yarn passes over what is called a snubber pin. The yarn is then wound up on to the lower bobbin. The geometry of the whole machine imparts a twist to the yarn during these operations.

Properties of Fibres

There are many physical properties of fibres which determine their ultimate usefulness and their application in a fabric for a specified purpose. One of the most fundamental is the ultimate strength of the fibre, for unless this attains a reasonable value the fabric would be of little use. The strength of a fibre is simply the weight per unit area which must be applied to cause it to break, and it can be measured in lb./sq. in. or kilograms per square millimetre or similar units. Another mechanical property of the utmost importance is the force required to stretch the fibre by a specified amount.

This is a measure of the extent to which, for example, a fibre might be stretched with loads far below the breaking point. It is of particular importance in dealing with ropes and belts for supporting weights or in transmitting power. There is a law in physics called Hooke's Law, which states that the extension of, say, a fibre is proportional to the load applied to it, and this is usually true for small extensions. The lower the slope of the line, the more difficult it is to deform the body and the higher the modulus of elasticity. The ratio of the load, say in lb./sq. in., to the fractional increase in length is the numerical value of this quantity and it, like the strength, is expressed in lb./sq. in. or in kilograms per square millimetre. This quantity is called the modulus of elasticity.

In the researches carried out to make man-made fibres the aim has been to try and get as high a strength as possible. It is interesting to compare the moduli of a number of fibres of different types.

Fibre	*Modulus*
Viscose rayon poorly oriented	35,000 lb./sq. in.
highly oriented	100,000 ,,
Acetate rayon poorly oriented	25,000 ,,
highly oriented	65,000 ,,
Nylon normal	70,000 ,,
highly oriented	140,000 ,,
Glass fibres 0·0005″ in diameter	150,000 ,,

From the table it will be seen that orientation of the molecules increases the modulus enormously, but there is a limit to this increase when orientation is virtually complete. The other interesting point is that although the fibres are chemically quite different, the moduli are similar in value. Even the modulus of the completely dissimilar glass fibre is close to that of nylon. There would thus appear to be some underlying reason for this similarity, and this raises in turn the problem as to the precise mechanism involved in breaking such a fibre. There are two different kinds of fracture. The first is that when the fibre breaks the molecules themselves are broken, in the sense that the bonds between the carbon atoms are actually severed, leaving

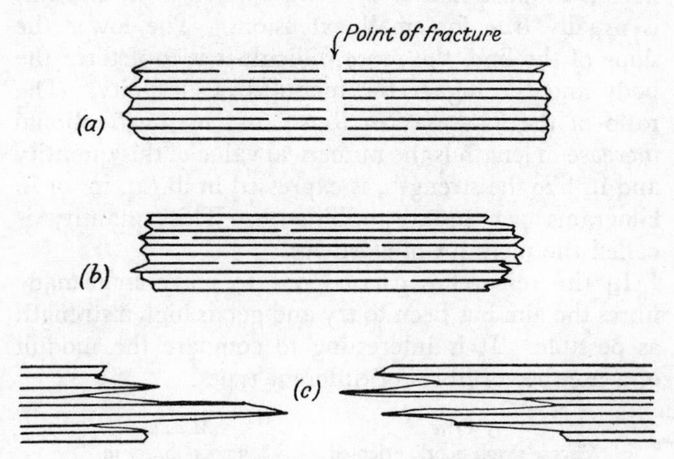

FIG. 18. The two ways in which a fibre might fracture.

fragments of molecules behind. This is shown in figure 18. On the other hand, suppose we consider a fragment of the fibre where there is quite a large number of end-to-end contacts between the molecules. When this portion is stretched the big molecules may slide past each other until final separation occurs. In the first kind of mechanism enough is known about the force holding carbon atoms together to calculate how much force is needed to break the bonds. Also it is easy to calculate from the density of the fibre how many such bonds there are likely to be in a square inch of fibre. The result is that it is estimated that the strength should be no less than 2,000,000 lb./sq. in., ten times greater than the strongest fibre so far produced. When the calculations are made for the second kind of fracture, then it is found that it is easier for the molecules to slide past each other, and the result is that the calculated strength is about 140,000 lb./sq. in. This is somewhat lower than the highest strength known, but it shows that probably a considerable amount of slip occurs before the fibre is broken. This idea is supported by the fact that the longer the molecule the stronger is the fibre, but the strength ultimately reaches a limit. There is therefore a tempting field for improvement if the ideas of figure 18 are correct. Many attempts have been made to push the strength to the limit, but one of the practical problems is that some of the desirable properties of the fibre may be lost. For example, continual flexing of the fibre, as would occur when it is incorporated in a motor-car tyre, would lead to fracture if the fibre becomes brittle on account of its very high breaking strength. A compromise has to be made having regard to the uses to which the fibre has to be put.

Effect of Moisture

The effect of water on the properties of fibres is of the utmost importance. If worn as clothing, the fibres should be capable of taking up some moisture evaporated from the skin in order to act as a controller of humidity. Secondly, most fibres are cleaned by washing in water, and it is important that the strength of the fibre is not materially reduced when being subjected to violent mechanical movement in any washing apparatus. All fibres take up water to some extent, the amount depending on the humidity of the atmosphere. At a so-called relative humidity of 65·0 per cent. wool takes up 15·0 per cent. by weight, cotton 7·2 per cent. and viscose rayon 15·0 per cent. On the other hand, nylon only takes up 4·2 per cent. and Terylene 0·5 per cent. Those fibres having the greater moisture uptake are the more comfortable to wear as garments because of this control of near-skin humidity. On the other hand, drying, after washing in water, is a much more prolonged operation for cotton and viscose than it is for nylon or Terylene, simply because the latter fibres take up so much less water. Similarly when wet, some fibres, particularly viscose, lose their strength to some extent, and so they have to be handled more carefully at this stage. Absorption of water produces another trouble. Nylon and Terylene are very much easier to electrify by friction than are wool, cotton or viscose. This ease of electrification leads to the fibres readily attracting dust particles. Such dust particles tend to become embedded in the fibre ultimately and are difficult to remove completely unless the fibres are washed frequently. However, this difficulty can be overcome to some extent by treating the surface of the fibre with films that prevent the accumulation of surface electric charges, but one of the current problems is to achieve a permanent finish of this kind which stands up to repeated washing.

Another factor of considerable importance is the abrasion resistance of a fibre, that is its ability to stand up to repeated rubbing without its being rubbed away. For reasons as yet unknown, nylon is particularly outstanding in this connection, and that is why it is used so extensively in stockings and in socks, especially at those points, e.g. heels, where abrasion is at a maximum. These properties are also of use in such applications as ships' ropes and hawsers, which are subjected to extremely high and sudden stresses and have to rub over capstans in a way that reduces ordinary hemp rope to a sorry state in a comparatively short time.

Elastic Nylon

In Chapter 2 it was seen that in solution a big molecule tends to coil up to some considerable extent as compared with its outstretched length. On the other hand, in a crystal the forces between the molecules that hold the crystal together are exerted to a maximum extent when the molecules are aligned parallel to each other. There is therefore competition between the tendency to coil up and the forces causing alignment. So, whether a molecule will be straight or coiled up depends on the magnitudes of these two forces. As the temperature is raised the forces between the molecules decrease because of thermal agitation and finally the solid melts and the molecules coil up. Nylon can be chemically modified to alter the magnitude of such forces. This is done by attaching to the chains an occasional bulky group so as to make it more difficult for the molecules to attract each other. The presence of these groups permits the molecules to coil up to a limited extent. If such a fibre is stretched it exhibits a property rather like rubber, for when the stretching force is removed the fibre jumps back quite quickly to its original length. This is elastic nylon. Unfortunately in so altering the structure of the nylon the strength of the fibre is reduced to some extent and does not compare with that of ordinary nylon; in consequence the uses for elastic nylon are somewhat restricted.

Crimped Nylon

There is another way of achieving the same result mechanically without impairing the ultimate strength of the fibre. Instead of allowing the molecules to coil up, the fibre itself is made into a coil of fine pitch by the following procedure. The drawn fibre is pulled quickly over a steel edge with a very small radius of curvature. The tension on the fibre causes considerable pressure to develop in the inside of the fibre where it touches the steel blade, whereas on the outside the fibre tends to be stretched. This imparts a permanent set to the filament, so that when the tension is released it coils up into a spiral. In weaving or knitting the filament it is normally stretched, and again after knitting the fibre coils up to a limited extent, so that the fabric shrinks to half its normal size. Such a woven fabric behaves similarly to one made of elastic nylon, with the advantage that when stretched to its normal extent the fibre will still have the strength of ordinary drawn nylon. The other practical advantage of garments made of crimped nylon is that their size is not critical—for example, socks or stockings will stretch to fit any reasonably sized foot easily. Similarly, other knitted garments possess a greater stretch capacity than, say, when knitted with wool, and hence fewer sizes need to be manufactured to meet a large range of measurements.

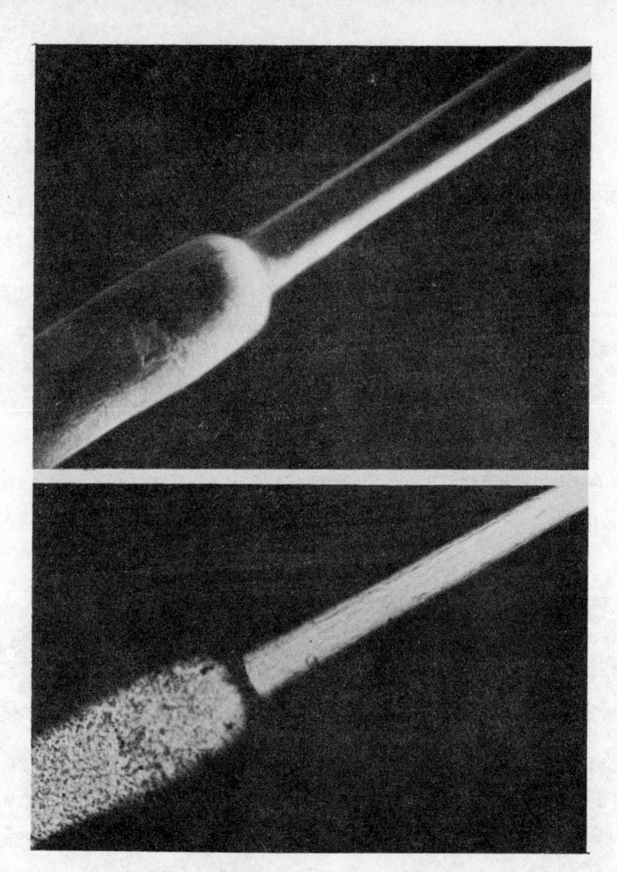

5*a*, *b*. Cold drawn fibres showing the necking that occurs. (See p. 86.)

Photographs by the late H. Emmett, I.C.I. Ltd., Alkali Division.

6*a*. Production of viscose filaments by the wet spinning method. (See p. 82.)

Courtesy of Messrs. Courtaulds Ltd.

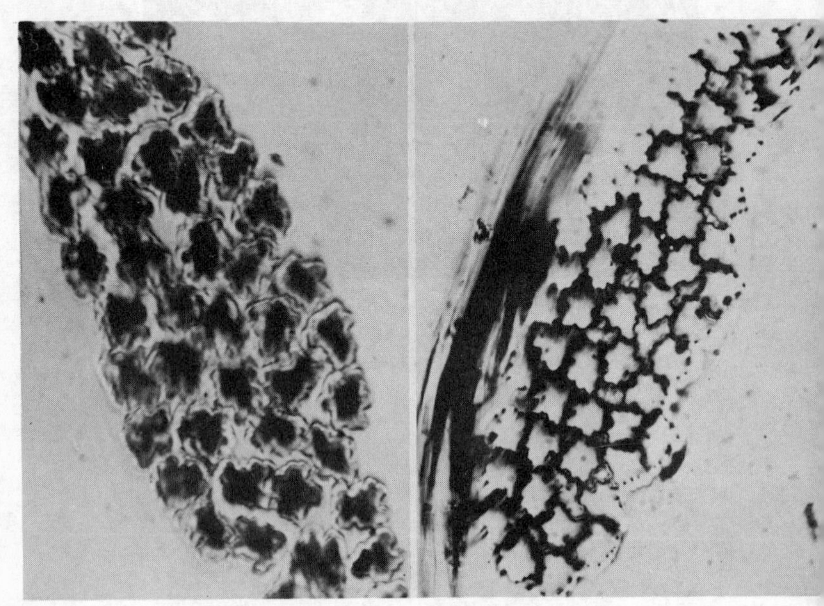

6*b*. The black areas show the resin distributed in the fibres. (See p. 98.)

6*c*. Shows the black coloured resin locate between the fibres, since it has not bee able to penetrate right inside them.

Photographs: Tootal Broadhurst Lee Co. Ltd., Research Dept., 56 Oxford St., Manchester 1.

Heat Setting of Fibres

Nylon yarn in the stretched state is in a rather unstable condition. If it is heated in boiling water for a few minutes it will decrease in length, because the molecules coil up to a small extent, in accordance with the ideas explained above. This is extremely important practically, for garments would shrink on washing, with disastrous consequences. It is therefore necessary to bring the fibres into a more stable condition such that when they are washed and ironed no changes of dimensions occur. This is done by the process of heat-treating the article, a stocking for example, in steam at temperatures much higher, e.g. 125° C., than it will be exposed to under normal use. The heat treatment is given when the stocking is stretched in a former of the right size.

This behaviour of nylon filaments in hot steam may also be put to use in making unusual effects in woven cloth. There is a form of fabric construction called seersucker, in which the rows of fibres in narrow bands are slightly puckered, whereas neighbouring bands are smooth. Such a fabric does not show up creases or folds, as it would if smooth. The structure is normally built into the cloth during the weaving operation. The same effect may be obtained in a nylon cloth by weaving it in the ordinary way partly from a heat-set and partly from a non-heat-set yarn. Initially the fabric is smooth and there is no obvious difference between the two kinds of yarn. When the cloth is steamed, however, the non-heat-set yarn shrinks and gives rise to the seersucker type of cloth.

Heat setting is of importance in another connection

—mainly in the production of permanently pleated garments. Terylene cloth is especially useful in this application. The pleats are ironed into the cloth at a temperature appreciably above that of boiling water. Under heat and pressure the filaments of the yarn are permanently bent into position. If such a garment is washed, even in hot water, the bend in the filaments is unaffected and the crease stays in position. This is quite unlike the performance of woollen garments, in which the pleat is ironed in in the presence of steam at a moderate temperature and very readily comes out.

Crease Resistance

If one compares a woollen and a cotton or viscose rayon garment in their ability to resist creasing it soon becomes clear that wool is very much superior in this respect. The wool fibre has a natural resilience which helps it to resist permanent creasing. Nylon and Terylene are similar in this respect. Cotton and rayon are, however, the least expensive of fabrics, and there is a constant endeavour to improve their properties by subsequent treatment of the fibre. The problem is to try to give some degree of springiness to the fibre without altering the otherwise desirable properties. This problem can be solved by the suitable use of big molecules. The chemistry of the process is rather complicated, but the requirements are quite plain. These are to stiffen up the fibre by the incorporation right inside it of small amounts of a fairly rigid type of big molecule substance. In Chapter 1 the process for making phenol formaldehyde resins—often popularly referred to as Bakelite, after the name of their discoverer, Baekeland—was described. It was explained that the first step involved the production of relatively small molecules which had built into them a certain residual chemical activity. This latter activity could be used at a subsequent stage to increase size and complexity when the material is transformed into a fully heat-hardened resin. A simple process can be used by replacing the phenol by another kind of molecule called urea having the formula

$$CO\begin{matrix} \diagup NH_2 \\ \diagdown NH_2 \end{matrix}$$

that is one can imagine that one of the oxygen atoms of carbon dioxide is removed and is replaced by two groups NH_2. With formaldehyde in the presence of acids and bases urea gives resins of the urea formaldehyde type. They are colourless and are used extensively for plastic cups, saucers, plates and many other domestic purposes. The reaction is similar in many respects to the phenol reaction, and the first step is

$$\underset{\text{urea}}{C{=}O\begin{matrix} \diagup NH_2 \\ \diagdown NH_2 \end{matrix}} + 2\ \underset{\text{formaldehyde}}{\begin{matrix} H \\ | \\ C{=}O \\ | \\ H \end{matrix}} = C{=}O\begin{matrix} \diagup NH{-}CH_2{-}OH \\ \diagdown NH{-}CH_2{-}OH \end{matrix}$$

Thus an alcohol is formed with two OH groups attached to the molecule. These groups are reactive and each attacks other molecules of urea thus:

$$C{=}O\begin{matrix} \diagup NH.CH_2OH \\ \diagdown NH.CH_2OH \end{matrix} + H_2NCONH_2 = \begin{matrix} NH{-}CH_2NHCONH_2 \\ | \\ C{=}O \\ | \\ NHCH_2OH \end{matrix} + H_2O$$

a molecule of water being produced on each occasion.

There is now an NH_2 group at the end of the larger molecule and as in the original molecule of urea, it too can react with yet another molecule of formaldehyde to give a further alcohol group. So the process goes on, leading to longer and longer linear molecules. Formaldehyde also attacks the NH groups in such a chain and provides a means of linking the chains together, as shown below, by the elimination of a molecule of water. In this state the resin becomes heat hardened and is insoluble and infusible.

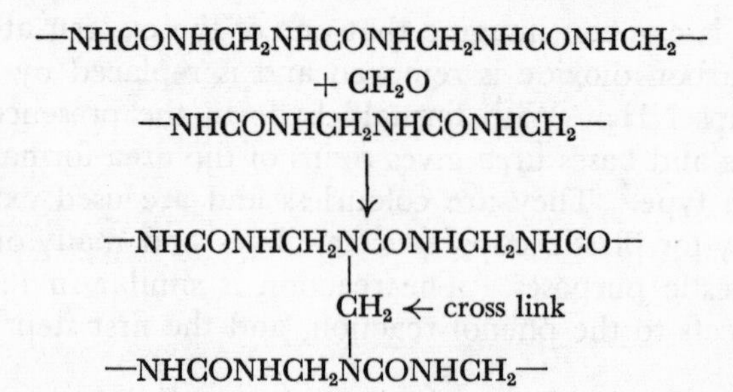

In making crease-resisting fibres the reaction is not taken to this stage—it is stopped at the first stage. Such a molecule is not only soluble in water but, because of its smallness, is capable of penetrating right inside the fibre. Thereafter the fibre is heated in a hot air chamber so that further molecular growth can occur. In Plate 6*b* it will be seen that the resin is distributed throughout the fibre cross-section, and Plate 6*c* shows the black-coloured resin located *between* the fibres since it has not been able to penetrate right inside them. It is like a kind of internal spring, and it is this reinforcement that prevents collapse of the fibre and assists it to regain its original shape when the deforming force is removed. To the touch such a stiffened fibre is similar to an untreated one. If the reaction described above goes too far before the fibre is treated with the solution, the resin stays on the outside. The fibre now has a rather harsh feel and does not possess the necessary quality of crease resistance.

Waterproofing

The cellulose fibres, whether of cotton or rayon, take up water readily, so that liquid water soon penetrates a fabric made from these fibres. To prevent this occurring, as is needed in shower-proof cloths, the traditional procedure is to coat the fibres with a layer of paraffin wax or similar material. This prevents wetting of the fibre, so that the water droplets cannot penetrate the finely woven cloth. At the same time moisture from the body can diffuse through the cloth as easily as with a normal piece of untreated fabric. The disadvantage of the process is that wax does not adhere to cellulose fibre and is removed by some kinds of dry cleaning. What is wanted is a means of chemically producing a waterproof layer of a suitable substance on the fibre. This can be done by making use of the process for producing silicones described on p. 41. The cloth is treated with a solution of the appropriate silicone, and it is then heated for a few minutes to a temperature of about 150° C. in order to complete the reaction. During this final process it is presumed that the compound becomes chemically bound to the fibres, so that it cannot be washed or rubbed off. Another incidental advantage of the process is that the fibres seem to remain cleaner for longer periods than the untreated variety. Since the layer of silicone structure is only a few atoms thick there is no appreciable change in the other properties of the fibre. The two processes of crease resistance and water repellancy can be applied to the same fibre without interfering with each other. The precise chemistry of the process has not yet been worked out, but a general picture of what happens is that we may regard the fibre, with its affinity for water, as consisting of a cylinder upon the surface of which there is a large

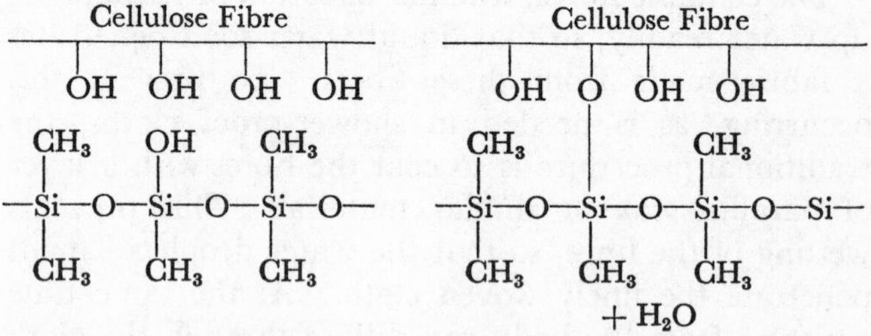

```
          Cellulose Fibre                         Cellulose Fibre
 ____________________________________      ____________________________________
      |        |        |        |              |        |        |        |
      OH       OH       OH       OH             OH       O        OH       OH
                                                         |
   CH3       OH       CH3                    CH3         |              CH3
    |         |         |                     |          |               |
 —Si—O—Si—O—Si—O—                          —Si—O—Si—O—Si—O—Si—
    |         |         |                     |          |               |
   CH3       CH3       CH3                   CH3        CH3             CH3
                                                      + H2O
```

number of OH groups. A silicone molecule is deposited on this surface and the structure is so chosen that some of the silicon atoms, instead of having two methyl groups, have only one methyl group and an OH group which will certainly orient itself close to the OH group of the fibre. When heat is applied a molecule of water is eliminated and an Si—O— bond made with the fibre. So in effect a chemically bound layer of silicone is formed on the fibre. Since the CH_3 group content of the layer is high, it behaves like paraffin wax in that water does not wet it and does not spread on such a surface, so that it becomes water repellant and water may easily be shaken from it. Nylon fabrics can be similarly treated, but the chemistry of the process is then rather different.

Fireproofing of Fabrics

One of the disadvantages of cellulose fibres as compared with wool, Terylene and nylon is their ease of combustion if brought into contact with a flame or electric fire element for a very short period. Combustion is so rapid that a garment made of such fibres can give rise to very serious and often fatal burns. The hazard is so great that all electric and gas fires must now be protected by suitable guards. However, there is another way of removing the hazard—by way of big molecules, utilising the fire-proofing qualities of phosphorus compounds. Again the problem is so to treat the fibre with a non-toxic inert phosphorus compound with a permanent finish that it does not appreciably affect the physical properties of the fibre. Phosphorus atoms can combine with three or five atoms of chlorine to give PCl_3 and PCl_5 respectively. In the crease-resistant process one of the essential pieces of the molecule to build up the big molecule is the group of atoms —CH_2OH. It is possible to introduce the grouping into a PCl_5 molecule to give the following structure:

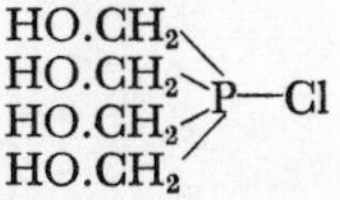

$$\begin{matrix} HO.CH_2 \searrow \\ HO.CH_2 \rightarrow \\ HO.CH_2 \nearrow \\ HO.CH_2 \nearrow \end{matrix} P—Cl$$

The OH-containing groups react readily with urea and other similar compounds. They also react with the OH groups in the cellulose fibre. The result is a big molecule containing phosphorus atoms as an essential element in its structure, and chemically combined with the cellulose so that the finish is resistant to mechanical removal by washing. When a cloth made of this material is brought into contact with a flame the cellulose will char, but the flame will not spread, in the sense that when it is removed combustion of the cloth immediately ceases.

CHAPTER

* 4 *

RUBBERS

Rubbers, or elastomeric materials, as they are now more generally called, form an almost unique class of substances. Solids, liquids and gases can easily be defined, and the reasons for the existence of these three states of matter is now well understood. Elastomers, on the other hand, cannot so easily be classified. Their outstanding characteristic is the ease with which they can be extensively deformed—such a rubber can be stretched to 800 per cent. of its original length without breaking and recover its original shape in a fraction of a second. Yet if the rubber is cooled to −100° C., it becomes a brittle solid, and if it is heated to 200° C. it can be treated almost as if it were a liquid. Thus elastomeric behaviour is a very temperature-dependent property. Further, it is not necessarily confined to substances which are normally regarded as rubbers, for elastomeric behaviour can be observed in some substances which would appear to be solids at room temperature. But the vital point is that all the elastomeric materials consist of aggregates of big molecules and the size of the big molecules is important in ensuring that elastomeric properties are fully developed. Most of the elastomers that are used in practice are long molecules with carbon atom backbones, but even this is not essential, for it is possible to replace some of the carbon atoms by sulphur atoms and still retain elastomeric properties. In fact one can go the whole way, and by heating ordinary sulphur, whose molecules consist normally of 8 atoms of sulphur S_8, convert it into long chains of sulphur atoms—elastic sulphur. This is simply done by heating ordinary sulphur until it is molten and heating rather above the melting point (120° C.), until the liquid begins to get extremely thick as the large sulphur molecules are formed. This liquid is then poured rapidly into water, and when cooled the material exhibits elastomeric properties. It is unstable in this state and, when kept, reverts to the ordinary variety of sulphur familiar in the laboratory. The silicone type of large molecules can also exhibit elastomeric properties to an extraordinary degree. For the exhibiting of elastic properties the chemical structure of the molecule is less important than its general long chain form. It is important, however, to find what is the factor that controls elastomeric behaviour. This matter can best be appreciated by going back to the fundamentals of molecule building. Suppose we consider a simple chain of carbon atoms and start off with two such atoms joined together by a single bond; then we proceed to add a third atom to the second. The question is where will the third atom be in space? Because of the fact that four similar atoms can be attached to carbon, there are only three possible positions for the third atom, and these three positions are fixed by the position of the second carbon atom. These three positions are identical, and hence the probability of the third atom occupying any one of them is equal. Then the process is repeated when the fourth atom is added. It too has three positions to choose from. In a typical rubber molecule there may be 10,000 such backbone atoms, and at each stage in the building up of the structure three possibilities exist. The number of possible configurations is therefore enormous. A photograph of such a molecular pattern (magnified about 100,000,000 times) is shown in Plate 7*a*. The tubes represent the bonds between the atoms, and the junctions of the tubes represent the positions of the centres of the carbon atoms of the chain. This model contains only 200 links. The large number of possible shapes is not the only feature of importance. Suppose we consider one particular bond in such a molecule, then it is known from a great deal of evidence from other quarters that it is possible to twist one half of the molecule with respect to the other. The amount of energy needed to do this is so small that the motion is practically free and the speed of rotation at room temperature may be many million rotations a second. The result is that the molecular configuration is changing extremely rapidly in the ideal example. There is another important consequence of the ease of rotation about the bonds joining the carbon atoms. If we could take hold of the ends of the molecule it would be a comparatively easy matter to pull it out, because all that is necessary is to rotate one atom with respect to another by rotating the bonds joining them together. In fact the molecule could be stretched out until all the carbon atoms are in the same plane. In this case the model would increase in length from about 2 ft. to 20 ft. If there were more links in a real molecule this stretching would be even greater. By such a stretching process the molecule assumes a very specialised shape and it will not retain this shape if the distending force is removed. In an elastomer a molecule of this kind is continually being bombarded by neighbouring molecules so that rotation round the bonds is continually being induced. If, therefore, the stretched molecule were left to itself it would at once coil up, not into the same configuration, but into a shape having the same overall dimensions as it had before stretching. The natural state of a long molecule is thus a fairly compact coil. This idea is supported by the measurements of the length of the molecules in solution by the light-scattering method described in Chapter 2. These ideal conditions are of course never attained in practice, for a variety of reasons.

The speed of rotation about the bonds is increased by increasing the temperature; correspondingly at low enough temperatures, for example at that of liquid oxygen at −182° C. the speed of rotation is slowed down. If a piece of natural rubber is cooled to this temperature it becomes so brittle that the rubber can be pounded to a fine powder by hammering. Another striking way in which to show the slowness of rotation round the bonds joining the atoms together at low temperatures, consists in rubbing a piece of stretched rubber over a block of solid carbon dioxide at 80° C. below freezing point. When the stretching tension is removed the rubber does not snap back into its original shape. If, however, it is plunged into warm water it does so immediately. This experiment may be repeated again and again with the same specimen. By changing the character of the backbone to the —Si—O— link of the silicone rubber this low temperature brittleness disappears to a large extent.

These changes in the shape of a rubber specimen are

accompanied by heat changes which are important in certain practical applications, for example in motor-vehicle tyres. From what has already been said it follows that the higher the temperature the greater the tension of a piece of stretched rubber. This effect is surprisingly large, and can readily be demonstrated by the instrument—shown in figure 19. The rubber band R and the metal spring S are stretched between two posts, the spring tension being such that the rubber is

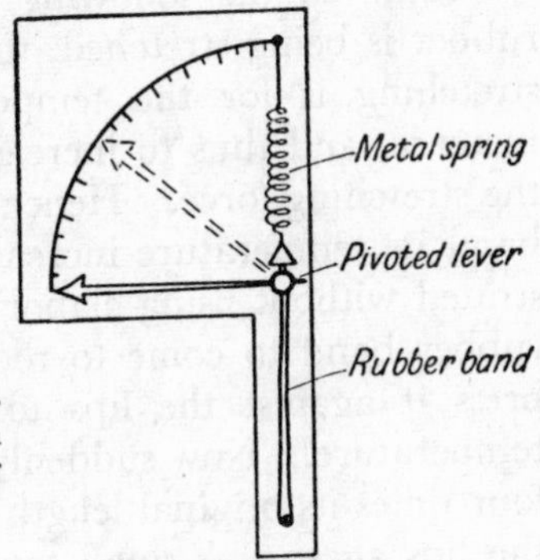

FIG. 19. Apparatus to demonstrate the effect of temperature on the tension of a stretched rubber band.

stretched by at least 100 per cent. A flexible link between the spring and rubber is wrapped round a roller F, to which there is attached a pointer to measure the angular motion of the roller. This rubber band is immersed in water at, say, 15° C., and the pointer adjusted to position 1. When plunged into boiling water the rubber immediately responds and the pointer goes to position 2, showing that increased tension has developed in the rubber.

In chemistry there is a general principle which is useful in predicting how a system, such as a piece of stretched rubber, will behave when the temperature is changed. The principle is simply that if the temperature of the rubber is raised, then the rubber will so change its shape as to oppose the temperature increase, that is change its shape so as to absorb heat, and therefore maintain the temperature constant if possible.

Similarly, if the temperature is lowered, the rubber will try to generate heat to keep its temperature up. If we apply this principle to the stretching of rubber we come to the following conclusion. Suppose the rubber is being stretched, then the way to oppose the stretching is for the temperature of the rubber to increase, and thus to increase the tension and oppose the stretching force. Hence when we stretch a rubber band its temperature increases. This can be demonstrated without using elaborate instruments. Allow a rubber band to come to room temperature and then press it against the lips to get an indication of its temperature. Now suddenly extend the band to, say, four times its original length and immediately press to the lips again. A small temperature increase will be detected. In order to do this experiment scientifically a thermocouple is inserted in the rubber, the couple being attached to a sensitive recording voltmeter which can be calibrated to measure temperature directly (fig. 20). If the stretched band is allowed to come into temperature equilibrium with the atmosphere and the tension is suddenly relaxed, then the voltmeter moves to the left, indicating a corresponding drop in temperature owing to absorption of heat from the surroundings. This heat energy is needed to make the rubber molecules rotate so that they can coil up into their original configuration in the unstretched state.

With this complete change in the shape of every molecule on stretching it might be thought that the specimen would never come back to its original shape. The reason that it does so quite accurately is due to the scale of the phenomena. Even a large rubber molecule when stretched is only about a ten thousandth of a centimetre long. Coiled up it is shorter by tenfold.

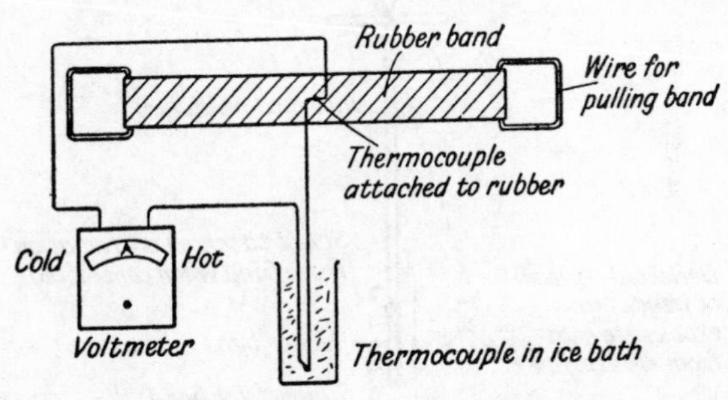

FIG. 20. Thermocouple experiments to demonstrate the change of temperature when rubber is stretched.

The specimen normally tested may be several centimetres in size. If we could look at the surface of the rubber with a microscope powerful enough to observe the shape of individual molecules, such a complete change of shape would be seen. But it takes place on such a minute scale. The average size of a group of molecules does not change, so this means a small element of volume containing thousands of molecules will remain the same in spite of the change of shape of the molecules themselves.

These heat effects can be even more strikingly demonstrated by two simple instruments which convert infra-red or heat energy from an electric fire into mechanical energy. The first is the rubber clock (fig.

21) and the second the rubber spoked wheel (fig. 22). The rubber clock consists of a long rod pivoted on a bearing near the upper end with an adjustable weight

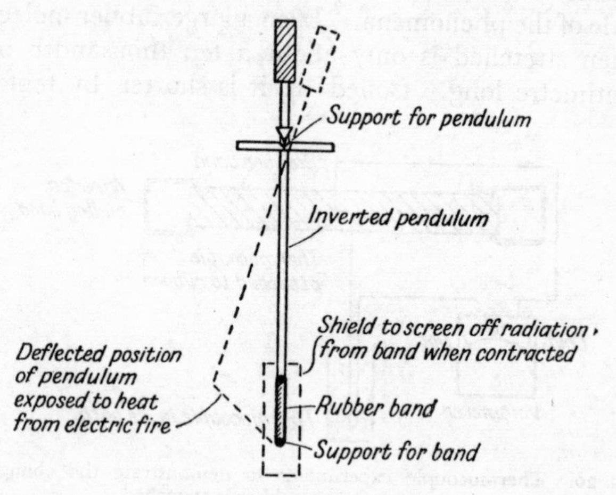

FIG. 21. Rubber clock.

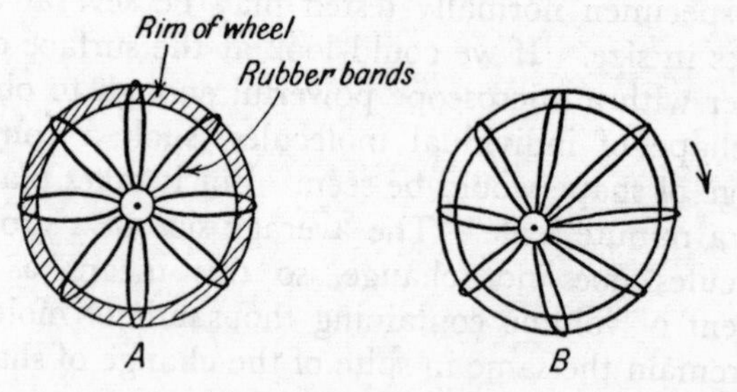

Fig. 22. Rubber wheel.

at the top so that the whole assembly is very slightly top heavy. The motion of the rod is restricted by a strip of rubber attached to the supporting pillar with

7*a*. Photograph of a molecular pattern. (See p. 105.)

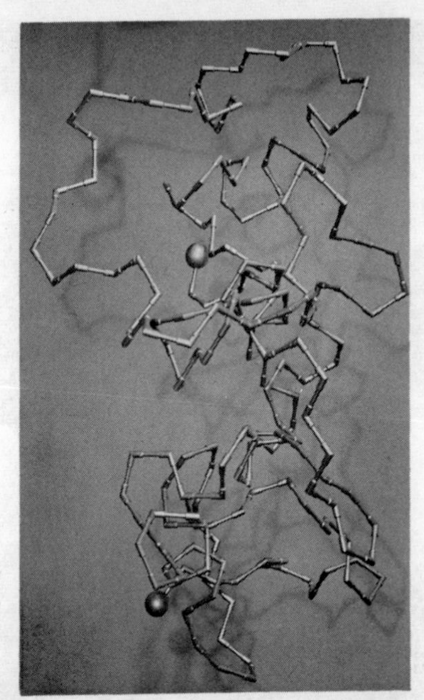

7*b*. Microphotograph of chain-like carbon black used for making conducting rubber. (See p. 115.)

Photograph by courtesy of Dunlop Research Centre.

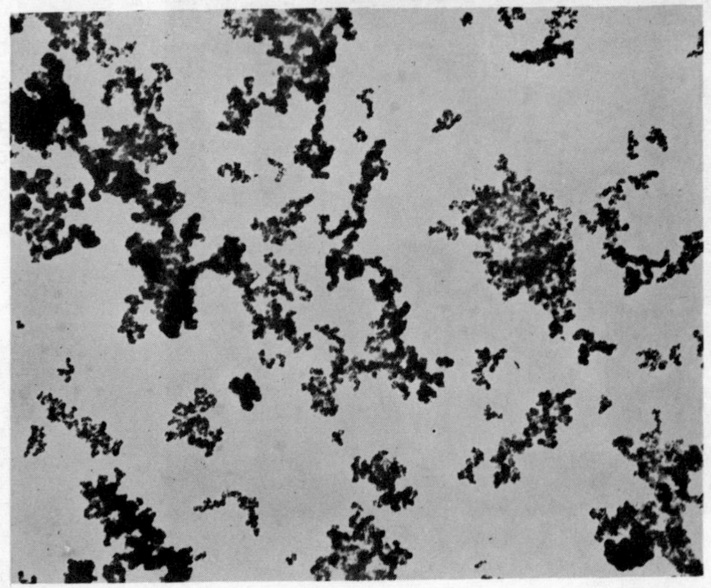

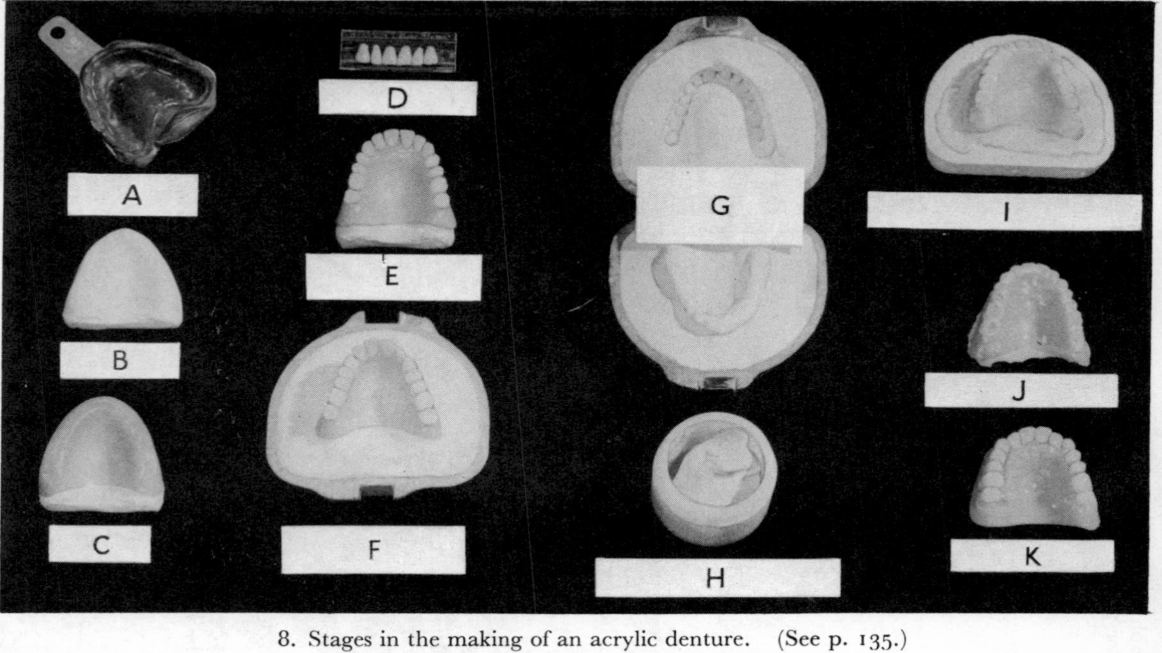

8. Stages in the making of an acrylic denture. (See p. 135.)

Photograph by courtesy of I.C.I., Ltd., Plastics Division.

A. Impression.
B. Model.
C. Bite.
D. Acrylic teeth.
E. Wax denture.
F. Wax denture inserted in plaster.
G. Plaster mould with wax eliminated.
H. Acrylic resin 'dough'.
I. Denture partially deflashed.
J. Denture deflashed.
K. Acrylic denture.

suitable bearings. When the rod is vertical, the rubber band is not stressed and it is shielded from the infra-red radiation from the electric fire. When, however, the rod moves to one side or the other, the rubber strip is exposed to the radiation and it tends to contract, and this pulls the rod back into a vertical position. The momentum so acquired carries the rod past this position, and the strip is once more exposed to the radiation. It retracts again, so the oscillations are maintained by the pendulum obtaining a suitable small impulse each time the rubber strip is exposed to the radiation. An even more striking way of showing these effects is by means of a wheel rim supported wholly by rubber spokes under tension. One side of the wheel is exposed to radiation from a fire. The spokes so exposed once more contract so that the centre of gravity of the rim is no longer concentric with the axis of the wheel. This causes the wheel to turn, thus allowing the heated spokes to cool and attain their original length. Fresh spokes are exposed until the wheel is turning steadily. Sometimes the wheel overshoots if the rate of heating does not quite match the speed of rotation, and the wheel may actually reverse for a moment or two. This is merely a demonstration of the nature of the effect, and the devices are so inefficient as converters of heat to mechanical energy that they cannot be used for any practical purpose.

The types of rubber used for the above-mentioned experiments are all vulcanised, that is, the rubber chains are linked together by cross bonds. The reasons for carrying out this operation will be dealt with later. The sheet rubber produced by the coagulation of rubber latex, whether it comes from a tree or a synthetic rubber plant, consists of straight-chain molecules not cross-linked in this fashion. This rubber behaves in quite an unusual way. If a strip of it is stretched by, say, 600 per cent., and the heat produced on stretching is allowed to dissipate so that the temperature falls below about 20° C., the rubber does not snap back to its original size when the tension is reduced. In fact when the stretching is carried out by hand it goes in slight jerks, and the process is rather like the cold drawing of nylon filaments. If the extended rubber is warmed in the hand it quickly snaps back to its original length. As in the case of nylon, rubber can also be crystallised, and the little crystallites can be drawn into line by such an extension process. The melting point of natural rubber is about 20° C., so these phenomena could be extremely awkward in practical applications. That the explanation of this behaviour is correct can best be shown by examining the rubber microscopically with polarised light, when there is immediate evidence of the alignment of the crystallites. However, this can be demonstrated more easily by examining the tearability of the specimen. With most varieties of rubber if a small incision is made in the specimen the crack so produced will readily extend if the rubber is stretched. With the unvulcanised rubber the effect depends on where the cut is made. If it is perpendicular to the direction of stretch, it is not easy to extend the cut; if, on the other hand, the cut is made at the end of the strip the rubber can be torn with the greatest of ease—very much in the same way that a banana skin is peeled off. This is due to the orientation of the molecules—in the first case one has really tried to cut across the rubber molecules themselves, which is difficult, and in the second the molecules are merely being separated from each other. The forces between the hydrocarbon rubber molecules are relatively low, so the process of separation is much easier than in the case of nylon. When the stretched rubber is melted there is no difference in tearability in any direction selected.

Vulcanisation

The discovery of vulcanisation was probably the most important advance ever made in rubber technology. It is the means whereby a product of little value became one of first-rate importance long before synthetic fibres and plastics had been actively thought about. It resulted from an urge to make satisfactory waterproofs. More than 100 years ago Macintosh exploited the idea of spreading rubber as a continuous film on to a supporting fabric, thus giving a composite cloth that was completely impervious to water. However, the rubber film suffered from the very serious disadvantage that when it got hot it became sticky. Further, the film would not stand up to abrasion—at this stage the macintosh might well have disappeared. Shortly afterwards Goodyear discovered that if the rubber were heated with sulphur the product still retained its rubberiness, but did not become sticky in use over long periods. At that time there was no basic scientific knowledge to provide an explanation of the effect of sulphur, but now it is known that sulphur acts as a cross-linking agent for the hydrocarbon chains, though its exact mode of action has eluded investigators even to the present day. Improved methods of vulcanisation by sulphur compounds and other methods have brought the process under very exact and strict control. But that in itself is not enough. By cross-linking the chains the rubber is prevented from crystallising at room temperature, while the frequency of cross links is still sufficiently low to maintain its elastomeric properties. If the proportion of vulcanising agent is materially increased, the product then is a hard ebonite. So one picture of vulcanised rubber is a kind of assembly of coiled springs laterally attached to each other, the whole being capable of extension many times. On account of this cross-linking a piece of rubber may be regarded as a single giant molecule. In this form rubber is not particularly resistant to abrasion or wear, which is of vital importance in tyres, and in addition it is subject to oxidation, which perishes the rubber and gives rise to a considerable fall in strength for a comparatively small amount of chemical change.

The abrasion resistance is improved by the incorporation of finely divided solids in the rubber. By far the best effect is obtained from carbon black, prepared either by decomposing hydrocarbons to carbon and hydrogen in a heated furnace, or by burning hydrocarbons in an oxygen-deficient atmosphere so that carbon or soot is produced in large quantities. When the conditions are suitably chosen, extremely finely divided particles are produced with an enormous surface area, for example 100 sq. metres/gram. This black is not just pure carbon—hydrogen forms part of the structure. It is believed that the rubber molecule does react with the surface of the black, so that the latter is not just an inert filler. So black vulcanised rubber is an extraordinary complicated structure of carbon particles dispersed in a three-dimensional network of carbon atoms. A great deal of attention has been paid to the way in which rubber abrades and wears, and it is believed that a cut is first made in the rubber, for example, by a stone, and that this cut is propagated when the rubber is flexed and finally a small piece of rubber is detached. There is no evidence that the rubber is rubbed away into volatile, liquid or solid products of small molecular size. The presence of carbon black prevents the formation of this cut and certainly its propagation. One of the problems in studying wear is to carry out the experiments under approximately the same conditions to those existing in practice, e.g. on motor-vehicle tyres. Practical tests have to be very prolonged to get an accurate measure of the amount of wear. Recently a much more elegant method has been adopted in which only the tread of a tyre is made radioactive to a limited depth. By measuring the radioactivity before and after a short trial it is possible to measure accurately the loss of rubber from the tyre-tread. Similarly these experiments allow the conditions of wear to be altered widely, so that the various factors causing the wear can be assessed much more accurately than has been possible by previous methods.

Normally rubber is regarded as an insulating material even when loaded up with about 30 per cent. weight of carbon black. However, for some applications it is desirable to make the rubber electrically conducting. This can be done by producing the carbon not as discrete particles but as chains of such particles, the conditions of carbon deposition being chosen to give a conducting filament (Plate 7*b*). When compounded into rubber these chains touch, and thereby permit the system to conduct to such an extent that any frictional charges that may be acquired by the rubber leak away comparatively rapidly. The practical applications are in two very different directions. In flight, aircraft can acquire very high electric charges. This can to some extent be dissipated by fixing discharge wires to the trailing edge of the aircraft wing, but there is considerable danger when the aircraft touches down. If ordinary insulating tyres were used, a spark might jump to earth from the under-carriage and maybe ignite a spillage of fuel in the vicinity. All aircraft tyres are therefore made conducting to cut out this hazard. The other important application is in rubber equipment in surgical operating theatres. Here rubber equipment (such as gloves, boots, pipes)

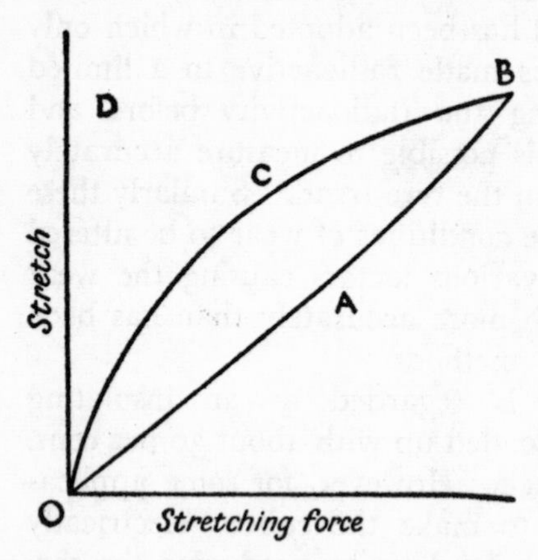

FIG. 23. Stretching of rubber—relation between stretch and stretching force.

is used for a variety of purposes. Again static charges are easily produced and might ignite escaping vapours of the anæsthetic. By using conducting rubber such charges are dissipated before the voltage can rise to dangerous values.

We now return to the question of the production of

heat in rubber, which is of particular importance in motor-vehicle tyres. Suppose a specimen of vulcanised rubber is stretched and the extension is plotted against the stretching force. A curve is obtained with a general shape OAB (fig. 23). When a force F moves through a defined distance E, work has to be done, and the work is equal to F $\times$ E. In this case the work can be represented by the area OABD. In rubber this energy is partly stored as potential energy of stretch and partly as heat developed on stretching. When the load is removed and the extension of the specimen follows the curve BAO, the same amount of work will be done by the rubber as is done on it when it is stretched, the potential energy and heat being used to restore the rubber to its original shape and temperature. This would happen in an ideal system, but most real systems are not ideal, and rubber is no exception. In fact the curve that the specimen follows is probably more like BCO. So the amount of work the rubber does is less than was done on it originally. This work done is represented by the area OCBD, which is smaller than OABD by the shaded amount. The rubber, because of its non-ideal behaviour, retains this energy as heat. If the rubber is subjected to repeated cycles of this kind more and more heat will be generated and, since the rubber is not a particularly good conductor of heat, the temperature of the rubber may rise so high that its abrasion resistance falls to low values and wear increases very rapidly. This is the phenomenon of heat build-up, and it is of particular importance in large tyres for buses and lorries. Whether the rubber is natural or synthetic the heat build-up must be kept at a minimum. The structure of the big molecule comprising natural rubber has the best performance in this respect—it is a good deal better than the standard synthetic rubber known by the general name GRS. Hence natural rubber must be used for the manufacture of large tyres. This heat build-up represents a waste of the power that is delivered to the vehicle by the engine and leads to an increased petrol consumption. This can be demonstrated very easily by the following simple experiment. If two rubber balls of the same size and weight, one of natural and the other of synthetic rubber of the type GRS, are allowed to roll down an inclined plane the natural rubber ball will go faster because the resistance to rolling is less than with GRS rubber. On the other hand, if the two balls are heated to approximately 100° C., they both run equally quickly, showing that heat build-up is a phenomenon dependent on temperature to quite a marked degree. Similarly the natural rubber ball will bounce more easily than the GRS one, but again at 100° C., the two types bounce equally well.

Special Purpose Rubbers

Elastomeric materials are used for so many different purposes that there is great scope for the building of molecules to suit a particular application—in fact tailoring the long molecule for a precise use. One of the disabilities of natural and GRS rubbers is that they swell in petroleum liquids and cannot be used in hose-pipes for the conveyance of petrol or oil. By a very slight modification of the structure of the large molecule, such as by replacing a CH_3 group with a chlorine atom, or replacing in GRS the

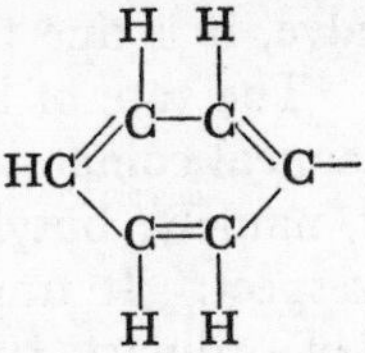

```
      H   H
      |   |
     C — C
   //     \\
HC          C—
   \       /
     C == C
     |    |
     H    H
```

group with a carbon and nitrogen atom in the form of a CN group, swelling can be so much reduced that these special-purpose rubbers can be used in applications where other types are completely useless. Similarly, rubbers are needed to resist deterioration when in contact with anti-freeze solutions used in motor-car cooling systems. Again a suitable structure may be chosen which is least swollen by such liquids.

Another problem concerns the hardening of rubber when used at sub-zero temperatures in northern latitudes or as the tyres of high-flying aircraft where very low temperatures can be experienced. In the second case embrittlement of rubber could have disastrous consequences when the aircraft lands. This problem has not yet been completely solved. By the incorporation of involatile liquids—plasticisers, as they are called—the hardening of rubber may be prevented, but only at the expense of a diminution of other desirable properties, e.g., abrasion resistance at high temperatures. Some rubbers, such as those derived from the silicones, are less affected by temperature in this respect, but in others they do not quite come up to requirements.

Gases such as oxygen and nitrogen penetrate continuous films of rubber—perhaps the most familiar aspect of this is that it is necessary to pump up car and bicycle tyres frequently. This is not due to the escape of air through the valve, it is due to leakage through the inner tube itself. The rate of loss of air depends very much on the chemical composition of the rubber. There is one variety, namely, butyl rubber, which is outstanding in this respect. It transmits air at only 1/10th of the speed of ordinary rubber, so that car tyres need only be inflated once in three months. The structure of this rubber mainly consists of the repeating unit

$$-CH_2-\overset{\displaystyle CH_3}{\underset{\displaystyle CH_3}{\overset{|}{\underset{|}{C}}}}-$$

A continuous rubber film does not transmit water vapour easily. A waterproof is not pleasant to wear over prolonged periods, since the moisture from the body cannot escape, as it does with a shower-proof garment. Successful attempts have been made to incorporate fillers such as clay and chalk into rubber so as to facilitate the transmission of water vapour but to resist transmission of liquid water. There is, however, a limit to the amount of filler that may be so incorporated because of the modification to the resultant film as far as wear and abrasion resistance are concerned.

Deterioration of Rubber

On exposure to sunlight and to air rubber is said to perish, that is it develops cracks and crevasses and the strength and abrasion resistance falls markedly, so that the useful life of the article is very restricted. This is due to oxidation of the rubber promoted by sunlight. As a result of the oxidation process the long chains of atoms are broken—not many links need to be broken before the properties of the rubber are affected. This means that a comparatively small amount of oxidation is sufficient to do considerable damage. Suppose there are 10,000 units in the structure of the rubber molecule, then the breaking of only one link is sufficient to reduce the size to a molecule containing 5,000 units, 10 links broken would bring the molecule down to only 1,000 units, yet it would be impossible chemically to detect such a small amount of oxidation. The effects of oxidation are better revealed by the much larger change in mechanical properties which it brings about. With natural rubber oxidation breakdown is extremely rapid, but there is a mechano-chemical effect as well, for the continual flexing or even stretching of rubber helps to accelerate the oxidation. When the rubber is filled with carbon black access of light is cut down, but this is not sufficient to maintain the physical properties over long periods. By the addition of specific substances known as anti-oxidants, to the extent of less than 1 per cent. by weight, oxidative breakdown can be brought under control. The reason for their effectiveness in such small amounts is as follows. Suppose the rubber molecule can be represented by the general formula $\begin{matrix} R_1 \diagdown \\ \quad CH_2 \\ R_2 \diagup \end{matrix}$, where R_1 and R_2 are parts of the rubber molecule, then the first step in the oxidation process is chemically very simple,

$$\begin{matrix} R_1 \diagdown \\ \quad CH_2 \\ R_2 \diagup \end{matrix} + O_2 = \begin{matrix} R_1 \diagdown \quad \diagup H \\ \quad C{-}O{-}O{-}H \\ R_2 \diagup \qquad \end{matrix}$$

in which the oxygen molecule simply slips in between the carbon and the hydrogen atoms.

Subsequently the oxidised rubber structure breaks down rather easily chemically with the breaking of carbon bonds in the rubber chain. By this time it is too late to prevent trouble, and the only way is to arrest the uptake of oxygen and prevent perishing of rubber. The job of the anti-oxidant is not to react with the oxygen, but to react chemically with the molecular fragments produced right at the beginning of the reaction. Fortunately there is a large number of such compounds, usually containing nitrogen, which preserve the rubber from perishing in this way.

There is another trouble that besets some types of rubber. Ozone (O_3) is an even more effective agent for attacking rubber than oxygen. It exists in the atmosphere in extremely small amounts, yet its effect is easily visible. It is not yet certain how the ozone is produced in the atmosphere and, contrary to popular belief, it is present just as much in the atmosphere of big cities as it is at the seaside. It seems to be most prevalent in the springtime. If rubber tyres on vehicles are exposed, ozone attack produces deterioration of the rubber, resulting in fine cracks. The rubber, at the apex of a crack, is strained to a considerable extent, so that the crack soon spreads and penetrates deeper into the body of the tyre. The trouble is particularly marked if the car is stationary for days at a time, but seems to be not nearly so marked when the car is used regularly. There are various methods of alleviating this trouble, but so far no satisfactory means has been found of eliminating it completely.

There are many elastomeric materials that are not affected by oxygen or ozone, for example butyl rubber and chloroprene rubber, the repeating unit in these structures being

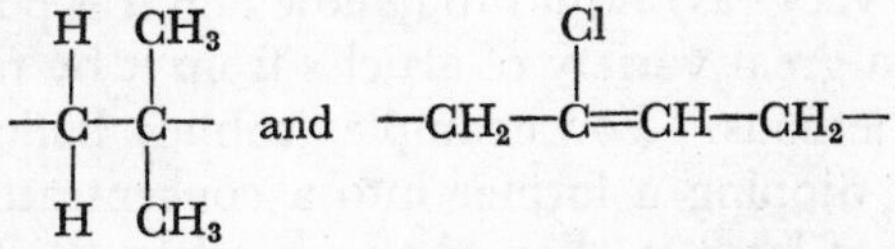

$$-\underset{\text{H}}{\overset{\text{H}}{\text{C}}}-\underset{\text{CH}_3}{\overset{\text{CH}_3}{\text{C}}}- \quad \text{and} \quad -\text{CH}_2-\overset{\text{Cl}}{\text{C}}=\text{CH}-\text{CH}_2-$$

respectively. But, as usual, these rubbers do not possess other properties which are of particular use for vehicle tyres.

With all these and many other requirements in mind the rubber technologist has an extremely difficult task in choosing the right kind of rubber for a particular job. He has to incorporate the right ingredients in the rubber to satisfy all the other possible requirements. In spite of the tremendous knowledge that now exists about the relationship between the chemical structure and the mechanical behaviour of an elastomer there is still enormous scope for further developments. In passing it may be mentioned that it is only within the past two years that it has been possible to produce chemically a synthetic rubber which has exactly the same constitution and internal structure as natural rubber and behaves in every respect exactly as does natural rubber.

Rubber Latex and its Applications

Rubber is obtained from the rubber tree as a fine suspension of tiny spheres about 10^{-3} cm. in diameter in a watery medium. This liquid is rubber latex. Sheet rubber is obtained from it by coagulating the latex by adding acid and salts to the latex, when the coagulated rubber separates as crumbs from the solution. It is then washed, dried and formed into sheets for further compounding. Rubber latex, however, is a very easy liquid to handle and it is possible to produce a great variety of articles from it by relatively simple methods. For example, rubber balloons are made by dipping a former into a concentrated latex. The film of latex is allowed to dry when the particles of rubber adhere to each other. Incorporated in the latex there are vulcanising agents, pigments and antioxidants, the first of which reacts chemically to cross link the film when it is heated. Similarly rubber gloves are produced by dipping a former into latex. Here, however, it is necessary to dip a sufficient number of times to build up a film of the required thickness. There is a great demand for rubber thread to make elastic, as it is popularly called. This is really rubber thread covered with a layer of textile material. One method of making the thread consists of wrapping a thin sheet of rubber round a cylinder and by means of a cutting tool literally slicing off spiral-fashion the thickness of thread required. An alternative and improved method is similar to that used for making textile fibres. A concentrated latex is allowed to flow through a narrow glass tube into a bath of acetic acid where coagulation of the latex occurs. At this stage the thread, though weak, can just be handled. It is then fed into long, temperature-controlled ovens, so that the rubber is vulcanised and finally emerges as a homogeneous, continuous and tough filament.

One of the most rapidly developing uses of rubber in latex form is in making foamed rubber for use as upholstery, mattresses and similar purposes. Here again it is a matter of coagulating the rubber latex under very carefully controlled conditions. To the concentrated latex there is added a coagulating agent called potassium silico fluoride, K_2SiF_6, and a small amount of zinc oxide. The mixture is rapidly beaten mechanically so as to suspend numerous small air bubbles in the latex. Beating is continued until the froth becomes stable but is still capable of flowing. At this stage it is poured into suitable moulds, which are placed in an oven to cure the rubber and remove the water from the system. The great merit of the method is the ease with which the most complicated shapes may be produced without the use of elaborate mould-making equipment.

CHAPTER

* 5 *

PLASTICS

Besides the elastomers and fibre-forming materials, big molecules give rise to an enormous number of materials that can be conveniently grouped under the term 'plastic'. These substances are capable of being moulded to shape under heat and pressure. Apart from convenience in manipulation, however, these materials have well-defined physical properties, which depend to a very marked extent on their chemical constitution. The result is that all sorts of requirements may be filled by selection from the range of materials which have so far been synthesised.

Fabrication of Plastics

The simplest method of moulding consists in placing a weighed quantity of plastic in powder form between the faces of a highly polished steel mould and heating and pressing until the powder flows into a homogeneous mass. The mould is allowed to cool and the object is removed. A diagram of the lay-out of such a press is shown in figure 24. The plates or platens of the press are heated by steam or electrically. These heated platens convey the heat to the mould itself.

9*a*. Pattern of stresses in a strained transparent plastic. (See p. 138.)

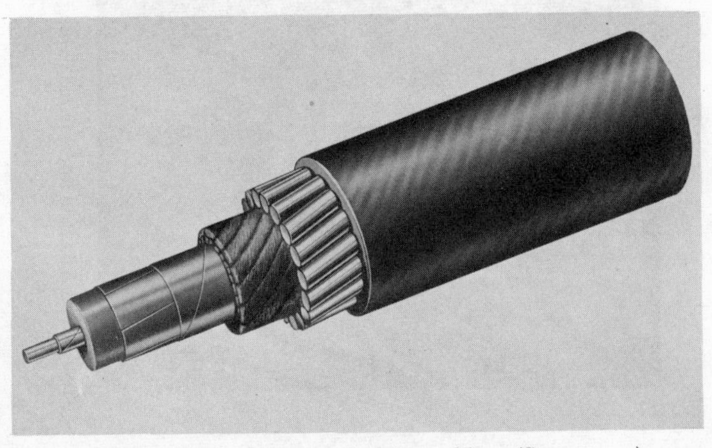

9*b*. Part of trans-Atlantic telephone cable. (See p. 140.)

Photograph by courtesy of Submarine Cables, Ltd.

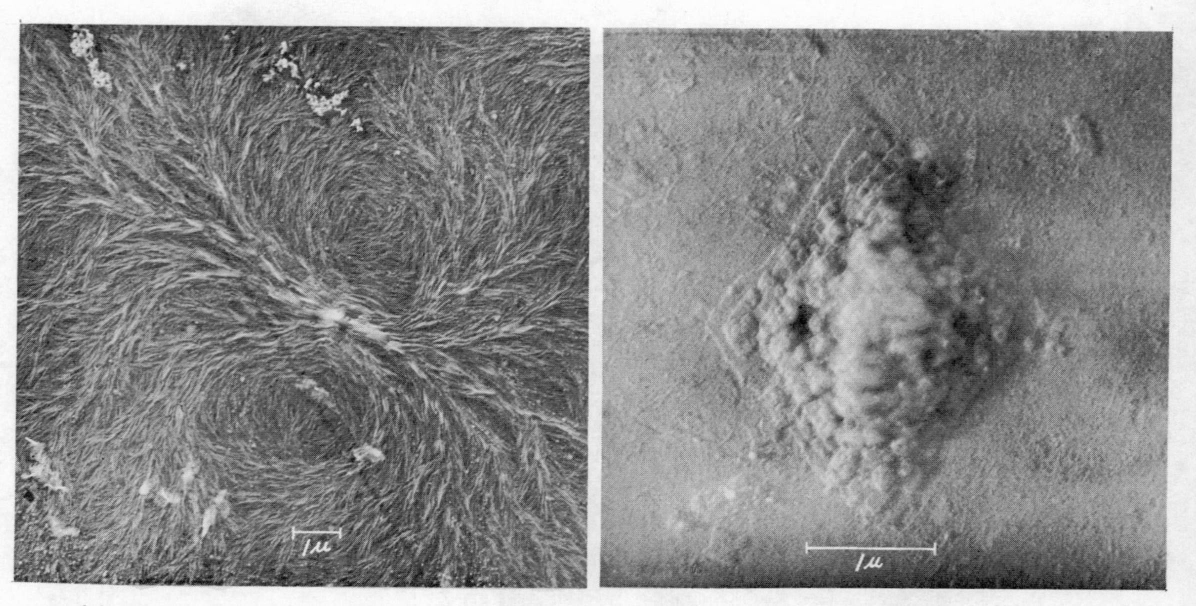

10*a* and *b*. Electron microscope photographs of crystallisation of polyethythene. ($1\mu = \frac{1}{1000}$ mm.) (See p. 138.)

The shape of the mould and the guiding pins of the mould open and closed are shown in the two parts of the figure. In order to obtain a satisfactory moulding a slight excess of powder is placed in the mould so that a very thin skin of material is extruded from the mould. Temperature of moulding depends on the chemical nature of the plastic and may range up to about 200° C. In order to get uniform mouldings,

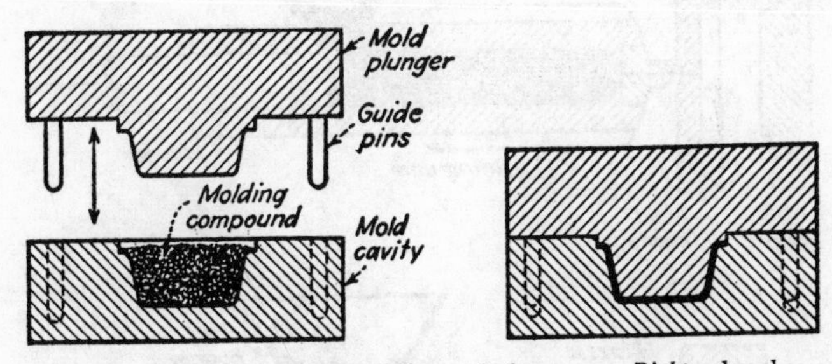

FIG. 24. Compression moulding. *Left:* open. *Right:* closed. *Reproduced from J. H. Du Bois: 'Plastics'.* (*American Technical Society, Chicago, 1945.*)

free of holes and imperfections, quite high pressures have to be employed, up to as much as 3 tons/sq. in. The large mouldings need very large and therefore expensive presses. The process is particularly suited to those resins which harden by heat. In this case heat is applied not only to enable the resin to flow but also to induce the completion of those reactions which lead to the formation of the big molecule and finally its cross linking into a three-dimensional molecule (see p. 37).

A modification of the method is that of injection moulding. Here the heating of the resin and the moulding of the resin are done separately. One practical advantage of using the method with those resins which remain plastic after heating is that it shortens considerably the actual time of moulding. The diagram, figure 25, shows the principles of operation. The powdered resin is fed from a hopper into a heated

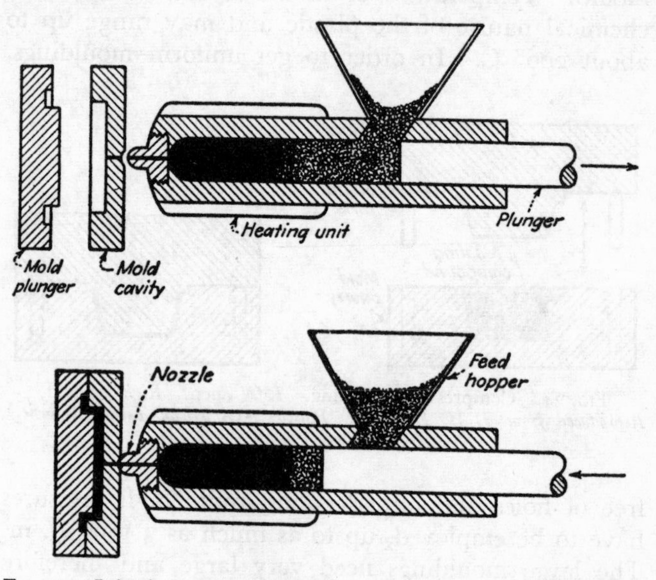

FIG. 25. Injection moulding. *At top:* mould open. *Below:* mould closed. *Reproduced from J. H. Du Bois: 'Plastics'.* (*American Technical Society, Chicago, 1945.*)

cylinder fitted with a motor-driven piston. After a short time—a few minutes usually—it becomes sufficiently plastic to flow under pressure. The molten resin is then injected through a nozzle into the mould, where it solidifies. Mechanical arrangements are made to open the mould, after which the plunger is withdrawn to admit a fresh charge of resin for the next operation. The whole operation can thus be rapid because the mould need not cool and it can be made wholly automatic by suitable devices. The moulding temperatures run up to values similar to those for compression moulding and the pressures reach to as much as 15 tons/sq. in. The result is that the machines are very large for mouldings of only a few ounces in weight. For small articles it is customary to make multiple moulds so that six or more items may be made during a single cycle of operation. The connecting links between them are then easily removed mechanically and the mouldings finished by suitable methods.

Extrusion Techniques

For many purposes plastic materials may be required in the form of sheets, films, rods or tubes. Here the need is for uniform cross section with some continuous process for unlimited production of material. This is best done by an extrusion machine similar in a way to that used for injection moulding. The principles of operation will be seen from figure 26. Again there is

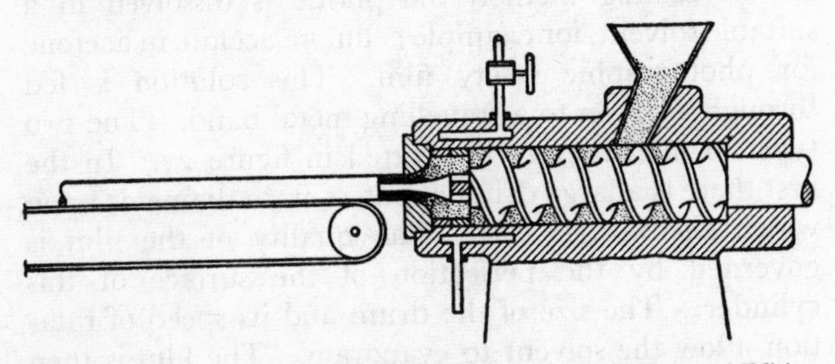

FIG. 26. Extrusion machine. *From: 'Handbook of Plastics', 2nd Edition, H. R. Simonds, A. J. Weith, and H. M. Bigelow, Copyright 1949, D. Van Nostrand Company, Inc., Princeton, New Jersey.*

a feed hopper, but inside the cylinder there is a closely fitting screw which forces the powder into a heated zone, where it becomes plastic. The semi-fluid mass is then forced through a die carefully machined to the requisite shape. On emerging, the section is rapidly cooled. If a tube is being formed, compressed air is admitted to maintain a circular cross section. With some plastics, for example polyethylene, the tube is actually blown into a bigger cylinder, and this is slit to form thin sheet.

The production of plastic film with a highly polished smooth surface for use as cinema film is a very complex business, requiring quite exceptional care in production, because the film must be extremely accurately made for running in high-speed cameras and projectors. Not less important is the dimensional stability of the film when stored over long periods of time. As with man-made fibres, film may be made by melt extrusion or solvent casting. In melt-spinning the molten material is extruded through a fine slit using a machine similar to that in figure 9, the extruded film being laid on a moving belt to cool. In the casting method the plastic is dissolved in a suitable solvent, for example cellulose acetate in acetone for photographic safety film. This solution is fed through a slit on to a travelling metal band. The two types of machine are illustrated in figure 27. In the first there is a large drum about 15 ft. in diameter upon which the film is cast. The quality of the film is governed by the perfection of the surface of this cylinder. The size of the drum and its speed of rotation allow the solvent to evaporate. The film is then in a state to be wound up into rolls. In the second type of machine the casting surface is a continuous metal band. Its function again is to allow evaporation of the solvent before the film is removed from its surface. In practice these machines are completely

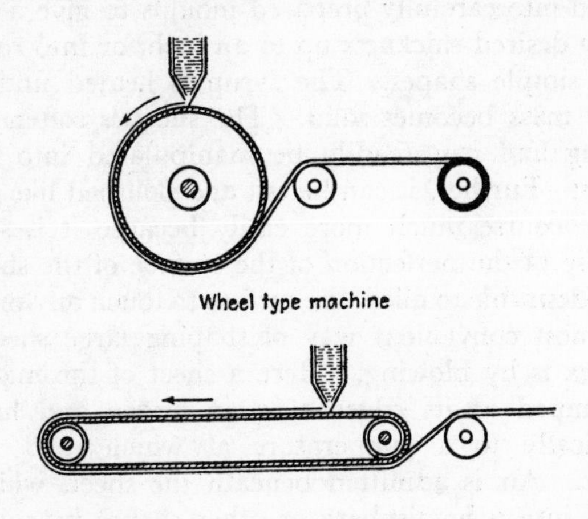

FIG. 27. Film-forming machines. *From: 'Handbook of Plastics', 2nd Edition, H. R. Simonds, A. J. Weith, and H. M. Bigelow, Copyright 1949, D. Van Nostrand Company, Inc., Princeton, New Jersey.*

enclosed in suitable containers, so that the evaporated solvent can be removed from the air stream and used over again.

Transparent Plastics

Apart from film-forming plastics there are a number of substances that yield completely transparent solids when fabricated under suitable conditions. As a result they can be used in place of glass in a variety of applications. The best example of the transparent plastics is Perspex. As already explained in Chapter 1, it is made by starting off with a highly pure, dust-free, transparent liquid which is transformed into a syrup—a solution of big molecules in the little ones. This is poured into carefully prepared moulds to give a sheet of any desired thickness up to an inch, or into rods or other simple shapes. The syrup is heated until the whole mass becomes solid. The sheet is softened by heating and can readily be manipulated into other shapes. Further, it can be cut and polished like glass, but of course much more easily because it is softer. Because of the perfection of the surface of the sheet it is not desirable to allow the surface to touch any mould. The most convenient way of shaping large sheets of Perspex is by blowing. Here a sheet of the material is clamped at its edges over an orifice and heated electrically to a temperature at which it becomes plastic. Air is admitted beneath the sheet, which is blown into a hemisphere or other shapes by suitable methods. Because of its lightness—its density is less than half that of glass—it is particularly useful as a window material in aircraft, and its strength is great enough to permit of its use in pressurised cabins of commercial machines. The complex structures can readily be built up of simpler components which can be stuck together with a cement of a solution of Perspex in chloroform. When the joint is made and the chloroform evaporated, a completely welded all-Perspex structure remains. The chemical nature of Perspex is such that it withstands long exposures to sunlight, air and moisture. On account of its transparency it does not absorb sunlight, visible or ultraviolet, and so no chemical change is brought about by this means. It is extremely resistant to chemical attack, and especially to oxygen, so it can be exposed for long periods outside without deterioration. These properties make it particularly suitable for outdoor fittings, such as the lanterns used for electric street-lighting.

The high transparency of the material suggests other applications. A rod of Perspex can be used to pipe light round corners. If a source of light is placed at the end of a long Perspex rod (fig. 28), some of the

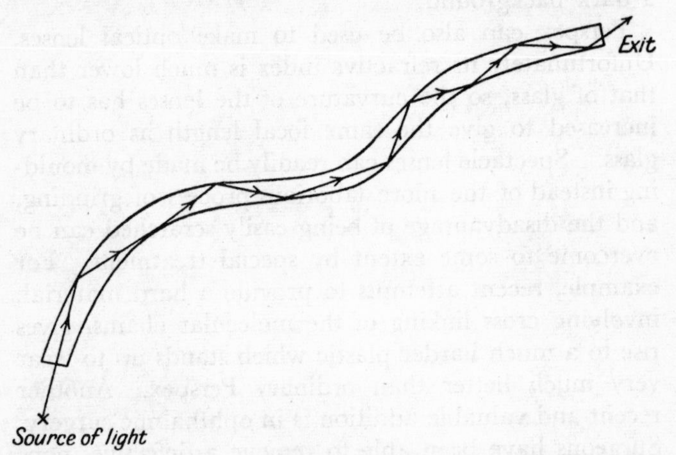

FIG. 28. Diagram to show how light can be piped along a Perspex rod.

rays will strike the surface of the rod. Provided the angle at which the rays strike is not too large, they will be completely reflected back into the rod. Bending of the rod is thus possible with this limitation to be kept in mind. Multiple reflection can take place without appreciable diminution in the intensity of the light. The result is that the light emerges from the end of the tube at a high intensity. This arrangement is of particular use in medical practice for illuminating regions of the body otherwise not easily directly visible.

If the surface of the rod is scratched at any point, internal reflection is seriously impaired and the light leaks out at this spot. This can also be used for decorative effects, for elaborate designs may be inscribed on a sheet of Perspex. The edge of the sheet is then illuminated by a strip light so that the light leaks out at the design, which shows up brightly against a dark background.

Perspex can also be used to make optical lenses. Unfortunately its refractive index is much lower than that of glass, so the curvature of the lenses has to be increased to give the same focal length as ordinary glass. Spectacle lenses can readily be made by moulding instead of the more laborious process of grinding, and the disadvantage of being easily scratched can be overcome to some extent by special treatment. For example, recent attempts to provide a hard material, involving cross linking of the molecular chains, gives rise to a much harder plastic which stands up to wear very much better than ordinary Perspex. Another recent and valuable addition is in ophthalmic surgery. Surgeons have been able to remove a defective, non-transparent lens from the human eye and replace it with one made of plastic. Although the lens is necessarily a fixed focus one, its lightness and chemical resistance make such an operation a practical possibility. Similarly the strength and inertness of the material have enabled surgeons to replace quite big bones in the human body by their plastic equivalents. But maybe the most widespread application on the medical side is the fabrication of dentures. The process of making big molecules can be adapted so as to permit the dental mechanic to carry out the job in the dentist's workshop and to make a perfect fit for the human gum. Again dimensional stability, strength and chemical inertness are essential in such an application. The process is an elaborate one, since both teeth and plate are made of plastic. The teeth are separately moulded by a compression process to the necessary variety of shapes and are coloured and tinted to provide a suitable match to existing teeth. The sequence of events and the results are shown in Plate 8. First, a wax impression is made of the gum. Next a model of the gum is made and then a wax denture with the teeth placed in position. This is then fixed in a plastic mould, and from this assembly the real mould is prepared. The teeth are inserted in the plastic mould and the remainder of the mould filled with resin 'dough'. This is a solution of big molecules and small molecules, together with a chemical initiator for the conversion of the small molecules into big molecules by the process described in Chapter 1. The dough is sufficiently fluid to fill accurately all the intricacies of the structure of the mould. The mould is then closed and heated. On cooling the complete denture is taken out and excess resin at the edges removed by grinding, to give the finished article.

Polystyrene

Perspex is not the only transparent thermoplastic material. There are many others, but for various reasons—including economic ones—another transparent material called polystyrene has become of great importance. The chemical reaction involved in making its big molecules is simply the union of many thousands of units in the following way:

```
              H                            ┌         H          ┐
              |                            │         |          │
   n  CH₂=C                  →             │  —CH₂—C—           │
              |                            │         |          │
              C                            │         C          │
            /   \\                          │       /   \\        │
         HC       CH                       │    HC       CH     │
         ||        |                       │    ||        |     │
         HC       CH                       │    HC       CH     │
            \\   /                          │       \\   /        │
              CH                           │         CH         │
                                           └                    ┘ n
```

This can be made in sheets, rods, etc., but its applications are in other directions. It is especially suitable for moulding by the injection process, since it has many advantages, such as speed of moulding. As a consequence it is used extensively for the manufacture of many familiar articles, such as toys and domestic equipment. Normally it is dyed and pigments and fillers are added, since it is not easy to attain a crystal-like clarity in this particular resin, as can be done with Perspex. It is, however, extremely resistant to chemical attack and retains its shape accurately after moulding. One of its disabilities in some applications is its brittleness—in fact if a moulding is struck sharply it rings almost like a piece of metal. Correspondingly, a sharp blow will cause it to break into fragments. However, there are methods of making it tougher by milling in a suitable proportion of natural rubber, which is mechanically dispersed in very fine particles in the polystyrene. This imparts a high degree of toughness without impairing the other characteristics, except the transparency.

Transparent resins also have an application in the engineering design of bridges and other similar structures. In designing an arch or beam with suitable supports it is important to make sure that no part of the system is subjected to a load that might lead to fracture of the metal in a limited region of the structure. Similarly, when an external load is applied it is equally important to know what parts of the structure are subjected to the maximum load. Much of these data can be obtained by calculation, but an alternative and complementary method makes use of transparent plastics in the following way. Suppose we have a source of light, S, which emits light-waves in which the electric vibrations lie in all directions perpendicular to the path of the light (fig. 29). Inserted in the beam

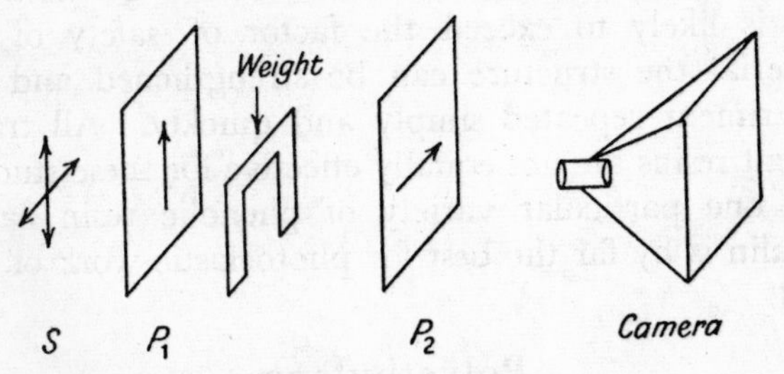

FIG. 29. Polarised light passing through a transparent plastic.

of light is a film of a substance called Polaroid. This is a plastic film with tiny crystals embedded in it, which are oriented in one direction. The orientation of these crystals filters out all the light which does not have the electric vibrations in the direction of the arrow. The light thus transmitted is then said to be polarised. The beam passes through a piece of transparent resin, R, and next falls on another sheet of Polaroid. If the crystals in this second film are pointing in the same direction as the first, the light will be transmitted. If on the other hand, the crystals are at right angles to those in P_1, no light will be transmitted. A camera, C, is focused on the system R, with the Polaroids at right angles. The piece of resin is then bent by applying a load. The effect is to rotate the direction of the electric vibrations to an amount depending on the strain in the resin. The result is that light from those parts which are strained will be transmitted through P_2. The kind of picture obtained is shown in Plate 9*a*. The closer the regions of light and dark, the greater is the strain in the resin. In practice, a plastic model is made of a section of the structure; this is loaded with suitable weights and photographs are taken to observe where the strain is greatest. If this is likely to exceed the factor of safety of the material the structure can be strengthened and the experiment repeated simply and quickly. All transparent resins are not equally effective for these studies, and one particular variety of phenolic resin called Catalin is by far the best for photoelastic work of this kind.

Polyethylene

For some considerable time it was thought that ethylene gas could not be made to join up to form long molecules, but at high temperature and pressures this can be done. Quite recently certain types of catalyst have been discovered which make this possible even at room temperature and atmospheric pressure. This plastic, called polyethylene or polythene, is rather like paraffin wax in appearance and feel—it is of course much stronger and melts at a higher temperature, 110–20° C., depending on the way it has been prepared. It can be moulded and extruded and spun into filaments in the same way as other plastics with comparative ease. It shows the phenomenon of cold drawing in an even more striking manner than nylon. This demonstrates that it can crystallise and that the crystals can be oriented by drawing. Some photographs taken with an electron microscope are shown in Plate 10. The second photograph shows the outline of a rudimentary crystal formed on the surface, which is perhaps one of the most direct pieces of evidence of internal molecular order in this plastic. But the most outstanding property of polyethylene comes in the electrical field. Because it is a hydrocarbon it is of course a good insulator, but in addition it is especially valuable as an insulator in the transmission of alternating currents at high frequencies. Many of the substances used as insulators contain electric charges separated from each other by dimensions about the size of the atoms—one hundred millionth of an inch—for example, in the structure

$$\begin{array}{ccc} & \mathrm{H} & \mathrm{H} \\ & | & | \\ - & \mathrm{C} - & \mathrm{C} - \\ & | & | \\ & \mathrm{H} & \mathrm{Cl} \end{array}$$

, the unit in the plastic called polyvinyl chloride, which will be dealt with later on. Each unit has a chlorine atom attached to a carbon atom. There is a separation of electric charges, in that the carbon atom is slightly positive with respect to the negative chlorine. If such an insulator forms part of a condenser, then when the charge in the plates alters sign, the $\overset{+}{\mathrm{C}}-\overset{-}{\mathrm{Cl}}$ part of the molecule will try to orient itself so that the positively charged carbon atom faces towards the negative plate and the chlorine atom towards the positive plate. So with an alternating current the orientation will alter with the change in the direction of the electric field. This movement of part of the molecule against neighbouring parts will be resisted by frictional forces and hence, if the orientation is continually changing, heat will be developed at the expense of the electric power transmitted through the condenser. The quicker the change of field, that is, the higher the frequency of the current, the more heat will be developed. With the high frequencies now used for television, radar and other communication systems, and for long submarine cables, the loss of power would be so great as to make these systems quite impractical if ordinary insulators were used. Polyethylene, on the other hand, has virtually no significant number of such positive and negatively charged groups, and so loss of electrical power in the insulator does not occur to such a great extent.

One of the most striking recent applications of polythene is in the transatlantic telephone cable. Such a cable costs many millions of pounds, and it is therefore important to be able to transmit many conversations simultaneously in order to make it economical. This is done by transmitting a very high frequency current along the cable. This, in turn, is modulated in the same way that speech current from a microphone modulates the output of a wireless transmitter. However, instead of one channel of modulation there is a large number, all spread suitably on the high-frequency carrier signal. Even with polythene such a high-frequency signal will be diminished in strength on passing along 50 miles of cable. At spaces of 37 miles, therefore, amplifying stations have to be inserted in the cable to increase the strength of the signal above the inevitable noise in any conductor. These amplifiers have also got to be supplied with power to operate the valves in them. In the manufacture of the cable the single copper conductor is sheathed by extruding the polythene mixture over the copper (Plate 9*b*).

Then an external layer of copper foil is laid on top of the polythene with subsequent layers of material used mainly for mechanical protection.

On account of its relatively low melting point, polyethylene can be manipulated relatively easily. It can be welded by a hot-air torch as sheets or pipes, and complex articles can be built up by a simple welding process at very moderate temperatures of about 150° C. This, in combination with its chemical resistance (it does not even dissolve in solvents at room temperature), makes it an ideal material to replace lead in drains, gutters, etc. If it is damaged or fractured and needs to be repaired, the simplest equipment can make thoroughly satisfactory joints and extensions. Its low melting point is something of a disadvantage in certain applications, and attempts have therefore been made to increase this once the fabrication of the article is completed. Chemically it is necessary to link up the hydrocarbon chains without otherwise impairing the nature of the network. If polyethylene is exposed to neutrons in an atomic pile, or to very fast electrons accelerated by a voltage of many millions, hydrogen atoms are knocked off the molecules, gaseous hydrogen is formed which escapes and the residual molecular fragments link up:

```
                   H   H   H   H   H   H
                   |   |   |   |   |   |
Before radiation  —C———C———C———C———C———C—
                   |   |   |   |   |   |
                   H   H   H   H   H   H

                           H
                   H   H       H   H   H
                   |   |   |   |   |   |
After radiation    C———C———C———C———C———C
                   |   |   |   |   |   |
                   H   H   H   H   H   H
```

If this cross-linking process occurs a few times along such a chain a three-dimensional network of atoms is built up and the material is rendered infusible without in any way impairing its electrical characteristics. The difficulty is to devise a method of carrying out such operations in a complex fabricated article having regard to the rather dangerous radiations which are needed to accomplish this chemical process.

Polyvinyl Chloride (p.v.c. for short)

When one of the hydrogen atoms on each alternate carbon atom in polyethylene is replaced by a chlorine atom, the resin so formed is called polyvinyl chloride, and its properties are entirely different from those of polyethylene. The softening point is increased to nearly 200° C. If it is heated to a much higher temperature it tends to decompose with evolution of hydrochloric acid. Similarly it is decomposed by sunlight, and the white resin becomes brown. The polymer itself is made by the emulsion method, and also by reaction of the pure liquid vinyl chloride. In both cases the polyvinyl chloride is provided as a finely divided powder which is the starting point for the fabrication of many articles. To prevent appreciable decomposition, stabilising agents are added, together with pigments, and the material is extruded as sheet, rod or tube, to form a rigid plastic. Like polyethylene, these elementary shapes can be joined up by a hot-air welding process into all sorts of complicated forms. The sheet is rigid enough to be self-supporting and, on account of its great resistance to corrosive fumes, it is becoming increasingly used for ducting and other similar purposes.

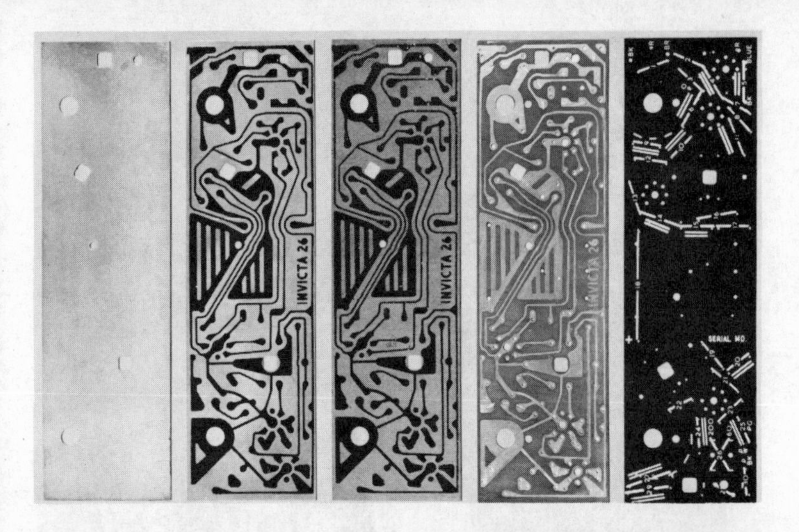

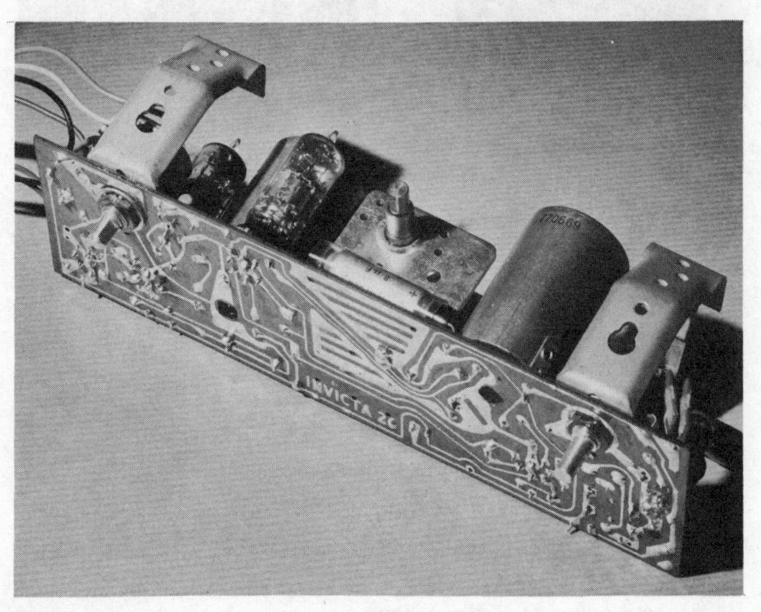

11*a* and *b*. Printed circuits. (See p. 151.)

12. The trueing of the wheels of the Royal State Coach by means of synthetic adhesives. (See p. 153.)

The work done on these wheels was carried out by Hooper & Co. (Coachbuilders), Ltd., in conjunction with Aero Research, Ltd., Duxford. Photograph by A. C. Cooper, Ltd.

13. Machine for testing the glueing of joints between aluminium strips. Taken during the Royal Institution Christmas Lectures. (See p. 154.)

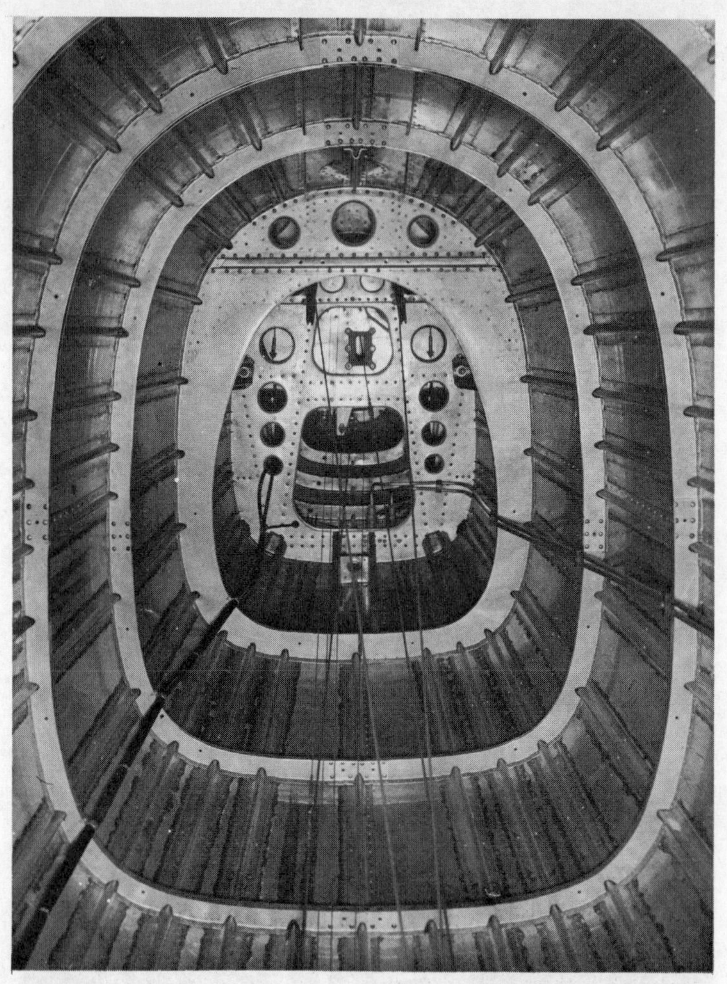

14. Part of a de Havilland Dove aircraft, showing glued reinforcement. (See p. 155.)

Photograph by courtesy of de Havilland Aircraft Co., Ltd.

The rigidity of the sheet is due to the strong forces of attraction between the neighbouring molecules. This plastic is therefore much too rigid for many potential applications. Although it is subject to chemical deterioration, it is much less so than is rubber —for example, its resistance to ozone is much greater. It is important, therefore, to find if there is some way of softening it and at the same time preserving its otherwise desirable properties. This introduces the idea of lubricants on a molecular scale to act between the chains of the big molecules. When a solvent is added to p.v.c. it softens, and the mass becomes easier to mould and extrude. This is simply because the solvent loosens the attractive forces between the p.v.c. molecules, and so permits the chains to slide past each other more easily—the solvent exerts what is called a plasticising action on the mass. Solvents for p.v.c. are rather volatile, so that the simple approach is not satisfactory because in use such solvents would readily evaporate. The problem is to find liquids, which are non-volatile and at the same time are compatible with the plastic itself, to act in this lubricating fashion. The majority of such substances are esters, formed by the interaction of an acid with an alcohol. In order to get non-volatile liquids it is necessary to use quite big molecules of both alcohol and acid. Typical examples are dioctyl phthalate, made from octyl alcohol, $C_8H_{17}OH$, and phthalic acid,

```
      CH
     /  \
   HC    C—COOH
   |     |
   HC    C—COOH
     \  /
      CH
```

obtained from the naphthalene in coal tar; and tricresyl phosphate, a compound of 1 molecule of phosphoric acid with 3 molecules of cresol (which is similar to phenol and is also found in coal tar). When such liquids are mixed with about twice their weight of p.v.c. the resultant product is a flexible material rather like soft leather. It is not elastomeric, but when stretched it yields appreciably, and then gradually retracts to its original shape, showing that the molecules may be uncoiled to some extent and the plasticiser permits them to coil up again rather slowly. If the material is kept stretched too long it tends to flow and take up a permanent set. The mechanical behaviour depends on temperature, and as the temperature is decreased the plastic becomes stiffer. The choice of the right plasticiser is thus quite a complicated matter; the exact structure can have an important effect—in fact the structure of both the alcohol and the acid have important influences. Recently it has been possible to build into the acid part of the molecule, groups which also act as stabilisers for the p.v.c. These groups are $—\overset{\diagup O \diagdown}{CH—CH}—$, but their exact mode of action is not yet known.

In the plasticised form the material may readily be made into sheets, and in this form it is used extensively for waterproofs, for making floor tiles, small hose-pipes, bags and similar travel articles. In the latter application one of its great virtues is its resistance to scuffing, or abrasion resistance. In this form it is sometimes necessary to join sheets and make seams. This is not easily done either by hot-air welding or by the use of solvent or adhesives, but there is another universally satisfactory method. In discussing the low electrical loss of polyethylene it was pointed out that the introduction of localised electric charges could lead to the production of heat in a plastic when used for electrical purposes. This is especially pronounced in plasticised p.v.c. and it can be put to good practical use. If two plastic sheets have to be joined, then the joint is gripped between the copper jaws of a clamp and a high-frequency current passed through the film. Local melting occurs, and in a few seconds the two parts are thoroughly welded together.

Sometimes the techniques described above are not suitable for the manufacture of certain articles. For example, complicated shapes are difficult to mould from plasticised sheet, and it is not easy to unite mechanically a film of plastic with a cloth to act as a reinforcement. This problem is overcome by the use of paste polymers. In this case the finely divided resin is dispersed in the plasticiser, the conditions being so arranged that the particles of resin swell to some extent, but the unimbibed plasticiser acts as a suspension medium for the p.v.c. particles. In this condition the system is a thick liquid, which may readily be poured into a complicated mould, such as that for a doll's head, where it penetrates into every crevice of such a mould. The excess liquid is drained off and the mould placed in an oven at about 150° C. After a few minutes' heating, the resin and plasticiser become completely mixed, forming a continuous film of plastic. On cooling, the article is removed from the mould without change of dimensions. The same sort of process is used in the manufacture of reinforced belting. If plasticised p.v.c. were used on its own, for a driving belt for instance, it would soon become permanently stretched. Reinforcement by a woven fabric is absolutely necessary for dimensional stability. The problem is to get the reinforcement right inside the resin. This is done by spreading on the polymer paste so that the fabric is completely enclosed. The composite material is then run through an oven to make the resin more homogeneous. Such belts are in continuous use for a great variety of purposes, for example for conveying coal and other minerals where abrasion resistance is of the first importance. Until a few years ago rubber belting was used in coal-mines, but its use proved hazardous, for occasionally the rubber became so hot that it could catch fire, with disastrous consequences if this happened to occur in presence of a dangerous concentration of fire damp in the mines. P.V.C. does not suffer from this disadvantage, but to make absolutely sure, the plasticiser that must be used is tricresyl phosphate. As with the fireproofing of cellulose cloth, so in the plasticiser, the phosphorus compound is particularly effective as a fire-proofing agent.

Polytetrafluoroethylene

A further slight modification to the ethylene structure, consists in replacing all the hydrogen atoms by fluorine atoms. These are only slightly bigger than those of hydrogen, and lead to a complete change in properties of the resin. The substance formed is called polytetrafluoroethylene (P.T.F.E.). Chemically the process is not done by replacement. Instead we start with small molecules and cause them to join up, as happens with ethylene itself: $n.CF_2 = CF_2 \longrightarrow (CF_2 - CF_2)_n$. This compound is one of the most stable and chemically resistant resins that have ever been made. It melts at about 425° C.—far higher than any other plastic. It is an extremely viscous liquid, and at higher temperatures it decomposes, the carbon atom backbone breaking down. It does not dissolve in any solvent, and it is un-attacked by strong acids and alkalis that would readily disintegrate and dissolve other resins. Only molten sodium will attack it chemically. The extraordinary inertness of the material makes it rather difficult to process. When the tetrafluoroethylene is made into big molecules the material can finally be produced as an emulsion in water. This can be coagulated to form films, and these can be heated to over 300° C. so that the tiny particles fuse together to form a more coherent sheet. Similarly the powder may be pressed together into compact masses, and sintering* used to get a continuous block of the material. In this form it is a soft, wax-like solid which can easily be cut and machined to shape. It can also be made into fibres, though none of the conventional fibre-forming processes can be used because of these rather unusual properties. It is believed that a process somewhat similar to that used for making rubber thread is employed, that is, an emulsion of the resin is allowed to flow through an orifice, and it is then coagulated. The weak thread is sintered into a continuous filament. The cloth woven from the filament is quite strong, and has phenomenal chemical resistance which makes it specially useful for the filtration of corrosive liquids. Another very important application is connected with atomic energy plants which have to deal with volatile compounds of fluorine such as uranium hexafluoride. The valves, pumps, glands and other chemical engineer-

* Sintering consists simply in heating the solid for some time below its melting point in order to make the granules adhere to each other.

ing equipment could not have been effectively used had it not been for the existence of the valuable properties of this particular resin.

Another unexpected property of the material is its low coefficient of friction. The coefficient of friction of most unlubricated surfaces does not normally fall below about 0·5. On the other hand, if the surfaces are coated with a thin film of P.T.F.E. the coefficient drops to as low a value as 0·07. Even if one surface is coated with P.T.F.E. the coefficient of friction is reduced. This can readily be demonstrated by comparing the time taken to come to rest of two ball bearings, one plain, the other coated with P.T.F.E., when set spinning on a clean watch-glass. The coated bearing keeps rotating for a very much longer period. Composite metal-P.T.F.E. bearings have been made, the P.T.F.E. acting as a kind of permanent lubricant that does not escape as would a liquid lubricant. P.T.F.E. has been used to coat the runners of skis, as it decreases friction, and therefore increases speed. On the other hand, sharp cornering is not so easy, owing to the reduced sideways grip on the snow.

Reinforced Resins

The combination of a resin or rubber with a fibrous material gives a composite substance, with a combination of properties impossible to get by any other method. The construction of a car tyre is an example. Another is wood, in which the cellulose fibres are glued together by means of a cement called lignin. As has already been mentioned, glass fibres exhibit an enormous breaking strength and if thin enough are quite surprisingly flexible, so that the question arises as to whether they can be used for reinforcing plastics. One of the essential conditions is that the resin shall stick to the glass, and, unfortunately, not many resins fulfil these conditions. The problem has been completely solved and a new class of material made available for many extremely useful purposes. The resin is made by a process similar to that for making Terylene, in that an acid and an alcohol are heated together and the molecules allowed to join up to a limited extent. In addition, the acid is chosen so that it possesses residual chemical activity which can be utilised at a later stage in the process. The structure of the resin in the first stage may be shown diagrammatically as follows. Here it will be seen that the carbon atoms

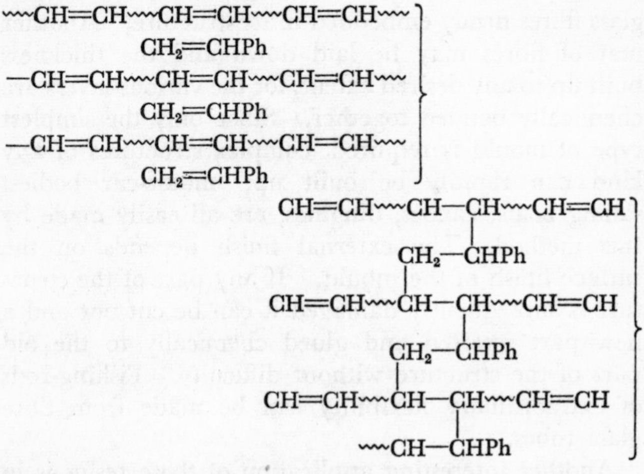

```
~~CH=CH~~CH=CH~~CH=CH~~ ⎫
          CH2=CHPh      ⎪
—CH=CH~~CH=CH~~CH=CH~~  ⎬
          CH2=CHPh      ⎪
—CH=CH~~CH=CH~~CH=CH~~  ⎪
          CH2=CHPh      ⎭

        CH=CH~~CH—CH~~CH=CH ⎫
                   |        ⎪
              CH2—CHPh      ⎪
               |            ⎪
        CH=CH~~CH—CH~~CH=CH ⎬
                   |        ⎪
              CH2—CHPh      ⎪
               |            ⎪
        CH=CH~~CH—CH~~CH=CH ⎪
                   |        ⎪
              ~~CH—CHPh     ⎭
```

in the backbone are occasionally joined by two bonds instead of one. This resin is then dissolved in a liquid called styrene, which we shall represent by $CH_2 =$ $CHPh$, where Ph stands for the group C_6H_5. To this liquid is added an initiator which causes the styrene to start growing into big molecules when left for a few minutes. Before the reaction starts, however, the liquid is poured on to a felt of glass fibre or on to a woven fabric. These mats may be placed in a simple wooden mould if particular shapes are needed. The glass–resin mixture may also be wrapped round formers to produce tubes or any other similar complicated shapes. In a few minutes reaction starts, heat is developed and the reaction then goes even faster. There is no need to apply pressure, for the resin is already in intimate contact with the glass. The styrene molecules in growing incorporate part of the resin in their structure, so that the whole mass sets to a strong and infusible three-dimensional resin with the glass fibres firmly embedded in its structure. Another mat of fibres may be laid down and the thickness built up to any desired extent, for the various layers are chemically bonded together. Since only the simplest type of mould is required, complex structures of any kind can rapidly be built up; motor-car bodies, sailing boats, canoes, dinghies, are all easily made by this method. The external finish depends on the surface finish of the mould. If any part of the structure is subsequently damaged it can be cut out and a new part inserted and glued chemically to the old part of the structure without difficulty. Fishing-rods of extraordinary flexibility can be made from fibre glass tubes.

Another interesting application of these resins is in the manufacture of press tools. In the fabrication of sheet metal for motor-cars, refrigerators, washing machines and the like, elaborate steel moulds have to be very carefully machined in order to press the steel sheet into the required shape. The cost of these tools is often a significant part of the price of domestic articles, especially if they are not made in very large numbers. These resins have an application in the sense that a very precise mould can be made and the resin shaped in that mould according to the methods mentioned above. In this way the cost of making the mould is materially cut down. Yet the strength of this composite material is so great as to permit one to shape steel sheets in exactly the same way as is done with the more conventional type of steel tools.

A much older-established method has been used for making composite materials of phenolic resins with paper, wood, asbestos and other fillers. In the paper-based process the paper is drawn into a solution of the resin in alcohol, then through an oven to remove the solvent. The sheets of paper are then cut to size and stacked between highly polished stainless-steel sheets. The whole assembly is then pressed and heated to complete the resin reaction. Probably the cellulose of the paper becomes to some extent bonded chemically to the resin. Light-coloured resins can also be added as a veneer to this layer, so as to give a finish which is suitable for table-tops and other domestic articles where stain and scratch-resistant surfaces are necessary.

One of the most interesting uses of laminated resins is in the mass production of electrical circuits for radio and other communication equipment. In this case a thin film of electrolytically produced copper is bonded to a sheet of the resin about 1/32-in. thick. This copper forms the basis of the connection between the components in the radio sets. A photosensitive coating of a special gelatine is spread on the copper, then a transparency with the required pattern is placed over this layer and exposed to a source of light so that the exposed parts of the gelatine are rendered insoluble in hot water. The 'print' is then developed with hot water, so that the soluble gelatine is removed from the surface of the copper. This exposed copper is then chemically removed by treatment with a solution of ferric chloride. Finally the hardened gelatine layer is removed, so revealing a complex pattern of flat copper connecting strips for the chassis of the radio set. Suitable holes are bored in the laminate and the transformers, resistors and capacitors are attached to the side remote from the copper with the connecting wire protruding through to the copper side. Finally the connections are made by immersing the copper side in a bath of molten solder, when simultaneous soldering occurs at once. The sequence of the process is illustrated in Plate 11.

Adhesives

Animal glue adhesives have been used to join pieces of wood together for many centuries. But in this field, too, synthetic materials have been developed which do the job better and quicker and do some things that would be quite impossible with the traditional type of adhesive. These glues are to a large extent based on formaldehyde-urea and formaldehyde-phenol compositions. The general principle of operation is that the glue as such is prepared by allowing the components to react to a limited extent, that is to say the molecular size is restricted, but in so doing each of the molecules retains a potential chemical activity. When the glue is applied to the surfaces to be joined and the joint made, heat and/or the presence of chemical catalyst produces further growth of the molecules so as to form a strong bond between the two surfaces. It is a matter for argument whether the glue is chemically attached to the surface. What is quite certain is that these synthetic adhesives give joints of far greater strength and reliability than those obtained by conventional glues. The glueing of wood is of vital importance in the making of plywood, in the manufacture of hardboard from wood chips or waste and in the fabrication of furniture. Here speed of setting is of importance to increase the rate of production, so the glue must be capable of penetrating the pores of the wood to a limited extent and it must be set by heat rapidly. These conditions have to be met, and yet at the same time a glue composition which is sufficiently stable at working temperatures is equally necessary. A striking demonstration of the application of the synthetic glues can be made in the following way. If two flat pieces of wood are taken, one side being coated with a thin film of glue and the other with a film of dilute hydrochloric acid as catalyst, then when the two are stuck together under pressure of a few pounds per square inch for a few minutes, the reaction is complete even at room temperature, and the joint so made is as strong as the wood itself.

One of the interesting applications of the new synthetic adhesives to an historical object concerns the Royal State Coach, built nearly 200 years ago. The iron-shod wooden wheels became uneven by as much as an inch, giving a very uncomfortable ride in the coach. The problem therefore was to true up the wheels and to provide a solid rubber tyre as a running surface. The original iron tyre could not be removed from the wheels, so a cotton bandage (Plate 12) impregnated with resin was wound round the tyre and the whole assembly cured in position by infra-red lamps. Next, the wheel was rotated past a cutter which removed the high spots in the resin/cotton layer until the wheel was truly circular. The tyre for the wheel was then made by bonding a strip of rubber to a steel strip with synthetic resins. Finally the steel/rubber strip was bolted to the original iron tyre as an anchorage. In this way a truly circular and quiet-running wheel was made, so that the State Coach could be used with comfort during the Coronation.

Synthetic adhesives can be used to bond metal to metal in an equally satisfactory way, and this method has important applications in making aircraft wings and fuselages, since it eliminates much of the riveting needed in building up such complex aluminium-alloy structures. For this purpose special heat-hardening resins are employed, and they must be used at pressures of the order of 50–100 lb./sq. in. curing at 150° C. for periods of half an hour. These conditions make it necessary to employ elaborate tools to keep the surfaces in close contact during curing. The joins so made are extraordinarily strong. In Plate 13 a joint-testing machine is shown, testing a simple lap joint between Dural sheets (Dural is an aluminium alloy). When this kind of test is carried out the metal is broken and yet the joint remains intact, showing that in the joining process strength is actually added to the structure. In aircraft construction the sheets of light alloy have to be stiffened before being attached to the frame of the fuselage. This is done by riveting what are called stringers along the surface. However, the process can now be done more satisfactorily by glueing the stringers in position. Plate 14 shows the inside of the fuselage of a de Haviland Dove aircraft made in this way. Large sections of the Comet aircraft are fabricated by using the same process. Another novel application is the stiffening of the leading edge of the wing of the Bristol Britannia aircraft, part of which is shown in Plate 15. The ducts formed between the leading edge and the stiffeners provide the path for the hot air needed for the de-icing of the leading edge of the wing. Thin aluminium foil can also be bonded into honeycomb formation between thicker sheets to give light and extraordinarily strong components which are also suitable for use in aircraft applications.

CHAPTER

* 6 *

POLYMERS

In the previous chapters we have dealt with substances made from big molecules to function as rubbers, fibres and plastics. In this chapter we shall deal with a number of applications of big molecules to problems that do not lie in these defined fields, but are none the less important and sometimes rather unexpected. These applications will serve to show how versatile big molecules can become. In Chapter 2 it was mentioned that the solution of relatively small amounts of big molecules in a suitable solvent could increase the thickness or viscosity many thousands of times, and that at higher concentrations the liquid could be almost solidified by this method. This can be done not only in solvents like hydrocarbons but also in water solutions. These solutions have a number of useful applications in technology and in medicine.

One of the most striking qualities that a solution of this kind exhibits is the resistance it shows to break-up into droplets. If an ordinary liquid is allowed to flow from the tip of a tube, the jet so formed very quickly breaks up into drops. Similarly if such a jet of liquid is subjected to a quickly moving stream of air, it breaks up into a fine mist. Such break-up is absolutely essential, say, in the carburettor of an internal-combustion engine or in the fuel-spray nozzle in a gas turbine, so that the fuel may burn quickly. But in other cases it may be necessary to prevent the jet from breaking up. This can readily be done by using solutions of high viscosity. Plate 16 *a* and *b* show photographs of ordinary liquids and thickened liquids of different viscosity falling freely, and it will be seen that the jet of the thickened liquid persists for a much longer distance. Plate 16 *c* and *d* show the difference in behaviour of a drop of these two kinds of liquids when subjected to a blast of air. The thickened liquid is broken up, but only into sheets of liquid, and not into fine droplets. This idea is also used in flame-throwers. Here it is essential to project a jet of hydrocarbon fuel for as great a distance as possible, for example from a tank, so that the burning zone can be directed towards the target and maintained there without travelling back to the projector orifice. A similar kind of effect is used in the preparation of lubricating greases for bearings. Here the hydrocarbon lubricant must be kept in the bearing if it is to do its job. On its own, however, the retention of the liquid would require elaborate seals on the bearing, and loss of lubricant could readily occur after prolonged use as such seals might tend to wear. Again, by thickening the liquid with big molecules—aluminium soap in this case—the lubricant can be formed into a gel which will stick to the bearing surface for considerable periods of time. In the automobile field there is another extremely interesting application in lubricating oils for engines. As a lubricating oil is raised to higher temperatures there is a big drop in thickness or viscosity. In designing the lubricating system of an engine, the size of the oil pump, the size of the oil-ways and the clearances of the bearings are important factors in determining the viscosity of the oil to be used. Even in this country, where temperature variation is not so large as in many countries overseas, it has been necessary to use two different kinds of oils for summer and winter use. In winter time the high viscosity of an oil at low temperatures makes it difficult to turn the engine, and therefore throws a heavy demand on the starter battery, leading to a shorter working life. The ideal lubricant would be one in which viscosity is independent of temperature. But this is a scientific impossibility, and in fact variation of viscosity with temperature is an inherent property of all liquids. However, the conditions can be much improved by the solution of big molecules of a type chemically related to Perspex, but so modified by attaching a long hydrocarbon pendant group to the molecule as to render such a material soluble in lubricating oils. The effect is to reduce the amount by which the viscosity decreases with increasing temperature. The basic lubricant itself is of much lower viscosity than the normal untreated material, but the addition of big molecules increases its viscosity to a considerable extent. The increase is so chosen that in winter and in summer the viscosity does not get too great nor too small for satisfactory lubrication. The continual circulation of the solution eventually leads to a diminution in size of the big molecules, but this is not practically important, for the oil has to be changed anyway long before this break-up becomes serious. Figure 30 shows some of the viscosity/temperature charts for winter and summer oils, together with those for thickened oils. One of the incidental advantages of such oils is that under running conditions,

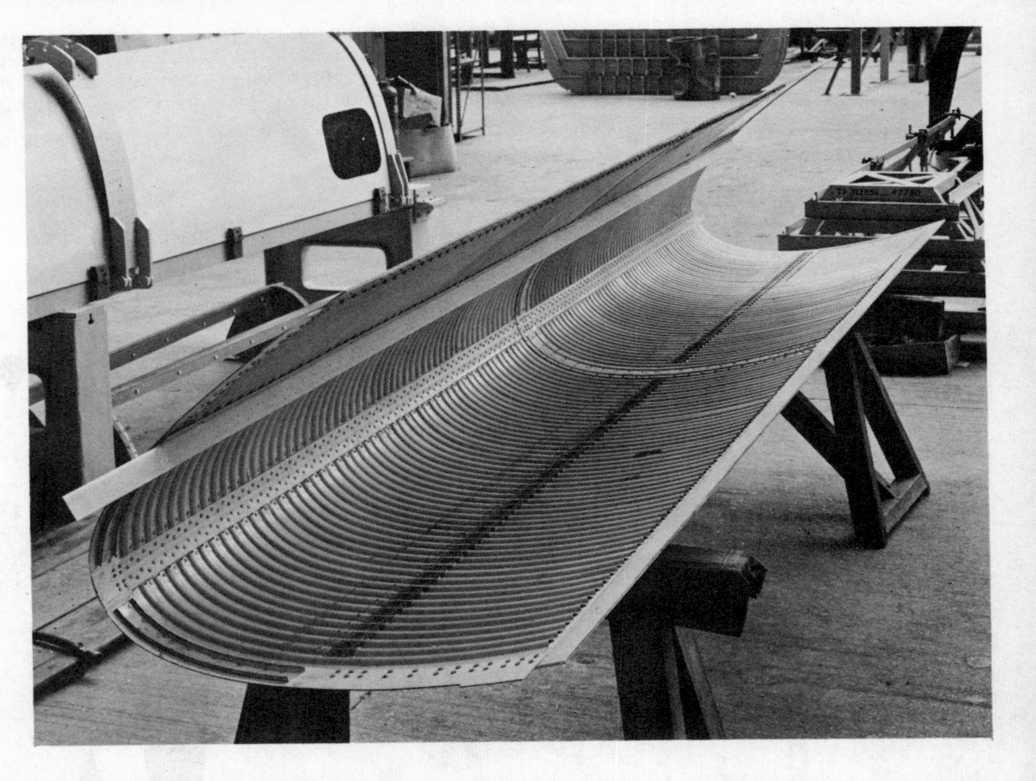

15. Leading edge of a Bristol Britannia aircraft, showing glued reinforcement. (See p. 155.)

Photograph by permission of Bristol Aeroplane Co., Ltd.

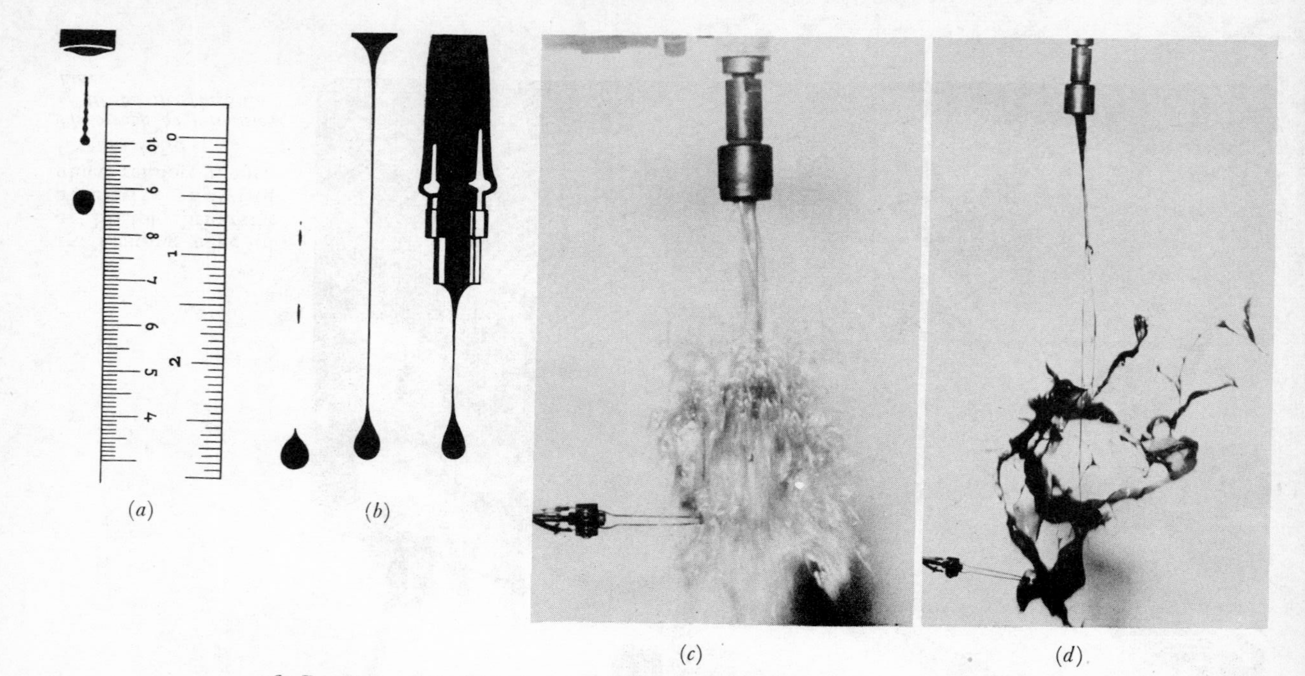

16. Break-up of liquid jets, using ordinary and thickened liquids. (See p. 156.)

The left-hand photograph (*a*) shows an ordinary liquid breaking up into droplets. The thickened liquid (*b*) forms long streamers with a drop at the bottom.

(*c*) This shows an ordinary liquid being shattered into fine droplets by a blast of air.

(*d*) This shows a thickened liquid receiving the same kind of air blast. Here the liquid breaks up into sheets.

especially from cold where considerable wear occurs, they seem to provide better protection and the corrosion which occurs on warming up an engine is to a large extent minimised.

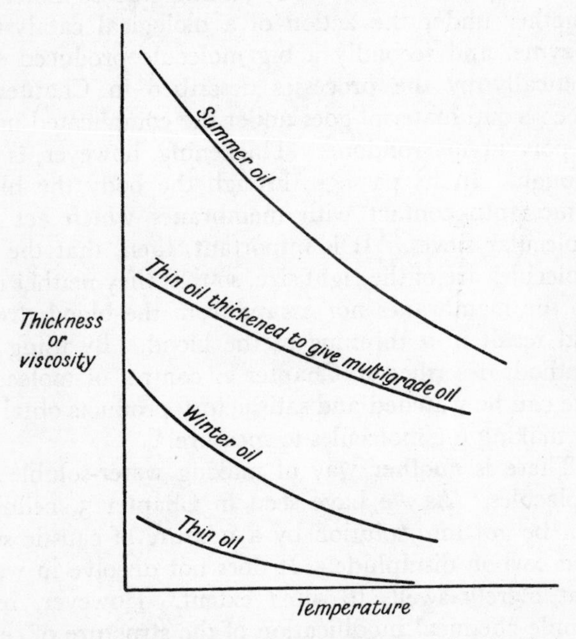

FIG. 30. Thickness of oils and so-called multigrade oils.

Another very different application of thickened liquids is in blood extenders. The popular saying that blood is thicker than water is of course true, and that it is so is due to the solution of big molecules in blood. If a human being accidentally loses an appreciable volume of blood it is useless simply to make up the lost volume by the injection of water into the veins.

However, the injection of a solution of sodium chloride in water thickened with big molecules is suitable where blood or natural blood plasma is not available. Two kinds of substances have been used in practice—first a big molecule made by joining glucose molecules together under the action of a biological catalyst or enzyme, and secondly a big molecule produced synthetically by the processes described in Chapter 1. The second material goes under the complicated name of polyvinylpyrrolidone. Thickening, however, is not enough. In its passage through the body the blood comes into contact with membranes which act like molecular sieves. It is important, then, that the big molecules are of the right size, so that they neither clog up the membranes nor escape from the blood stream and result in a thinning of the blood. By using the methods described in Chapter 2, control of molecular size can be watched and satisfactory products obtained by making the molecules to measure.

There is another way of making water-soluble big molecules. As we have seen in Chapter 3, cellulose can be got into solution by a mixture of caustic soda and carbon disulphide. It does not dissolve in water—it merely swells to some extent. However, by a simple chemical modification of the structure of cellulose it may be made soluble. Cellulose is an alcohol, and it may be represented by the symbol ROH. On treatment with caustic soda this becomes RONa,

$$ROH + NaOH = RONa + H_2O.$$

Acetic acid, CH_3COOH, can be altered slightly by replacing one hydrogen by a chlorine atom to give chloroacetic acid, $ClCH_2COOH$. This readily reacts with the soda cellulose, $RONa + ClCH_2COOH =$

$RO{\cdot}CH_2COOH + NaCl$, the cellulose thereby being converted into a weak acid which may be neutralised to give the sodium salt, $ROCH_2COONa$. This substance, commercially called 'Courlose', is freely soluble in water, in fact a 1 per cent. solution by weight forms a jelly. Such solutions have important applications as thickening agents in the preparation of foodstuffs, such as ice cream and similar confections, as they prevent the formation of crystals of ice during the making of these products. Courlose can also be used for cosmetic creams based on water, and even as an adhesive for sticking wallpaper. It is used for the sizing of textiles and in paper-making as a finish for the paper. Its presence improves the handling quality of clay in the pottery industry, and in oil-well drilling the properties of the drilling mud are improved by adding it in small quantities.

The structure of the substance in solution depends, however, on the acidity of the medium. The sodium salt in water is diagrammatically shown in figure 31 (*a*). Like other simple soluble salts, it is ionised in solution into Na^+ and $R{-}OCH_2{-}COO^-$ ions. The result is that the big molecule acquires a number of negative electric charges. These charges, distributed along the backbone of the molecule, repel each other, with the result that the molecule is stretched out to a considerable extent, partly due to these electrical effects. If the solution is modified by adding, say, hydrochloric acid, the cellulose acid is re-formed and the molecule loses its electrical charge, because this acid does not split up into ions to any appreciable extent. The picture of the cellulose acid molecule is shown in figure 31 (*b*). There is an immediate fall in the viscosity of the solution because the molecule attains a more compact shape. The effect is completely reversible, for if the solution is made alkaline again with caustic soda, the molecule is stretched out and the viscosity increases once more. So by using the presence of an electric charge in a molecule its shape can be materially altered in a water solution.

FIG. 31 *a* and *b*. Effect of an electric charge on the shape of a molecule in solution.

This idea has been further extended by considering the problem of producing mechanical energy directly from chemical reactions. This transformation can, of course, already be done by taking electrical energy from a primary cell to drive an electric motor, but an electric current is an essential link in the process for the conversion of chemical into mechanical energy. To do this directly it is necessary to make a fibrous material that is not soluble in water but is capable of acquiring and losing an electric charge in the manner indicated above.

This can be done by cross linking the acid molecules so that they only swell in contact with water. The procedure for making such a fibre consists in dissolving a commercially available polyacid (Krilium) and a water-soluble thickening agent in water and drawing

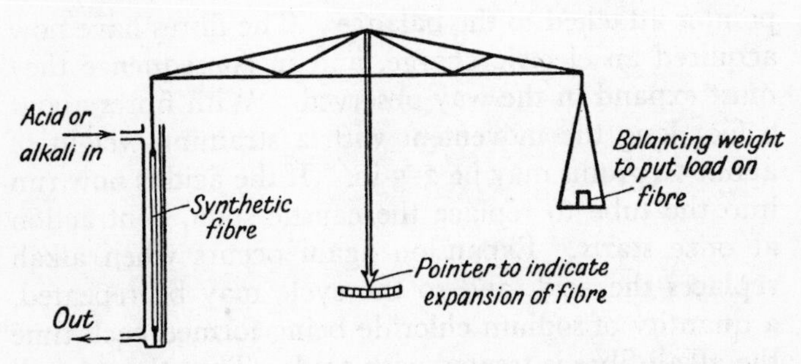

Fig. 32. Direct conversion of chemical into mechanical energy.

fibres from the solution. Bundles of these fibres are then heated for a short time. At this stage the fibres can be drawn so as to orient the big molecules to a somewhat greater extent. Finally, by further heating to above 100° C., cross linking occurs and the fibres then become insoluble in water. A bundle of such fibres is then fixed on to the apparatus shown in figure 32. One end of the fibre is attached to a glass cylinder filled with suitable inlet and outlet tubes for the addition of acid or alkali or distilled water. The other end is attached to the beam of a balance. At the other end of the beam there is an ordinary balance pan with a weight to keep the fibres taut. Distilled water is added to the cylinder and the fibre allowed to come to equilibrium with the water. Next, the cylinder is filled with a 5 per cent. hydrochloric acid solution, and a few minutes are needed for the system again to come to equilibrium. In this state the acid form of the fibre is produced. Next a 5 per cent. caustic soda solution is put into the cylinder, and within a few seconds the fibres expand, and go on expanding for several minutes, as indicated by the pointer attached to the balance. The fibres have now acquired an electric charge, and in consequence they must expand in the way observed. With fibres about a foot long the movement with a straining weight of about 10 grams may be 2–3 in. If the acid is now run into the tube to replace the caustic soda, contraction at once starts. Expansion again occurs when alkali replaces the acid, and so the cycle may be repeated, a quantity of sodium chloride being formed each time the alkali fibre is treated with acid. Thus the over-all chemical reaction is a neutralisation of hydrochloric acid by caustic soda in this rather indirect sort of way. In principle such a machine could be made automatic, so that at the end of each part of the cycle acid or alkali could be allowed to flow into contact with the fibre. Similarly the oscillating movement of the fibre could readily be converted into rotary movement. The efficiency of the process would be extremely low—less than 1 per cent. of power would be generated for the chemical energy expended. However, this sort of experiment is really the beginning of the subject called mechanochemistry, that is the mechanical effects that are brought about by changes in the chemical environment of big molecules. Examples of the phenomenon in reverse, so to speak, have already been mentioned, in which mechanical work on the system can induce chemical reaction to occur; as in the effect of ozone on rubber, an effect which is particularly noticeable when the rubber is stretched.

One further point of great biological interest is the question of the mechanical action of muscle. Here chemical energy is produced by an oxidation process and the response is extremely rapid—very much more rapid than can be obtained by the synthetic system described above. It has in fact been suggested that the muscle action may occur by such electromechanical process. Certainly this is one way of converting chemical to mechanical energy, but it is not yet clear whether animal muscles actually work by this mechanism.

The polyacids used to make the mechanochemical fibres have an important commercial application in soil chemistry, and go under the name of Krilium. Some soils possess the undesirable property of being fine and friable powders when dry, and slimy muds when wet. When dry they do not retain enough moisture essential for plant growth, and when wet they become so waterlogged that sufficient drainage of the soil does not take place to facilitate the growth of roots of plants. These awkward properties can be modified by the incorporation of as little as 1 per cent. of polyacid into the soil. This is most strikingly seen when to a typical mud there is added a small amount of polyacid. On stirring in the powder, the mud seems to dry up and the whole mass forms soil granules, which constitute a much more suitable medium for plant growth. Water will now readily drain away, so that waterlogging is completely prevented. In some parts of the world the soil structure may be such that heavy rain will wash away the surface soils to such an extent as to lead to serious loss of fertile ground. Soil conditioners can prevent such dangerous conditions arising and so avert the erosion which is specially critical in these locations.

The conversion of a large molecule to a polyacid can be done in another kind of way. One substance, polystyrene, is a pure hydrocarbon—it does not dissolve in water and a polished sheet of the transparent material is not wetted by water. This is sometimes a disadvantage. For example, if the material is used as a transparent resin for eyeshields, condensation of moisture will impair vision. This can be overcome by treating the surface with fuming sulphuric acid. The basic chemical reaction is simply $RH + H_2SO_4 = RSO_3H + H_2O$, where RH represents the hydrocarbon resin. The result is that an acid group is attached only to those parts of the big molecules exposed on the surface. In a way the surface becomes water-soluble, but because the water-soluble part of the molecule is anchored by the remainder of the resin, no actual solution occurs. Such a surface treatment is permanent, but of course can be removed by sufficiently vigorous polishing of the surface by means of an abrasive.

Ion Exchange Resins

If finely powdered polystyrene is sulphonated sufficiently it dissolves completely in water. However, if the polystyrene is cross linked by suitable methods, then if sulphonated to the same extent, it merely swells in water. This material is similar to the synthetic muscle. By suitable treatment of the same polystyrene it is possible to introduce basic groups, such as NH_2. These solid acids and bases have a variety of important applications in chemistry, and for a reason that will become clear later they are called ion-exchange resins. The basic ideas in all these applications may be illustrated with respect first to the acid resin which we may

$$\text{represent as}\quad \begin{array}{c} O^{\ominus} \\ | \\ R{-}S{-}O \\ | \\ O \end{array} \begin{array}{c} \\ \\ H^+ \\ \\ Na^+ \end{array}.\quad \text{In other words, it is}$$

almost equivalent to an insoluble type of sulphuric acid, the negative part of the sulphuric acid molecule being attached to the body of the resin. Suppose the resin is suspended in water, then in the neighbourhood of this negatively charged part there is a hydrogen ion, H^+. If, however, another ion, such as sodium, Na^+, is also present in the solution, then there will be attraction between the Na^+ ion and the negatively charged resin. Which positively charged ion will be more closely associated with the resin will depend partly on the attractive forces between the ions and partly on the concentration of the ions in solution. So if we start off with water and the hydrogen form of the resin, in which the only free positive ions are H^+, and then begin to add Na^+ ions as a solution of caustic soda in water, some of the H^+ ions attached to the resin will be displaced in favour of Na^+ ions. Thus the resin will remove Na^+ ions from the solution. If the resin is packed in a column and the alkali is added from the top, the liquid emerging from the bottom will not contain any Na^+ ions at all, until all the negatively charged positions are neutralised, and then of course caustic soda solution will emerge. If now we add to the top of the column a solution of barium hydroxide, $Ba(OH)_2$, then the Ba^{++} ions will tend to displace the Na^+ ions, so that caustic soda will emerge from the bottom until all the negatively charged sites are satisfied by Ba^{++} ions. In a similar way, using a positively charged basic resin, it is possible to withdraw negatively charged ions from the solution and replace one ion by another, depending on their relative affinities for the resin. These ions having the highest affinity are most easily removed from very dilute solutions. This method can therefore be used for the removal of ions from solution. In the later stage these ions so taken up may be displaced by other more strongly absorbed ions and the displaced ions readily collected in a much more concentrated form. There is another factor of importance. These materials are usually manufactured in bead form, and most of the ionisable groups are right inside the bead, so that the ions have to penetrate into the bead to get taken up. Ions vary enormously in size, from two hundred millionths of an inch in diameter up to 10 times that size. Whether the ion will be taken up will depend on the pore size of the bead, so that further discrimination can be made between ions by the purely mechanical effect of filtering them out in this kind of way. Pore size of the resin can equally be controlled by the mode of cross linking and the density of the ionisable groups.

The oldest established use of such materials is in the softening of water, that is the removal of Ca^{++} ions that react with soap to give a precipitate of calcium soap. Here a material negatively charged and containing sodium is used. When the hard water enters the column, the Ca^{++} ions displace the sodium ions. When the column is completely saturated with calcium, the calcium ions can then be displaced by treatment with a strong solution of common salt until it regains the sodium state again. In this case a naturally occurring mineral called zeolite is used, with a network structure rather similar to that of the synthetic resin. In a similar way most ions of metals can be removed from dilute solutions because of their very high affinity for the resin. Copper, for example, can readily be removed from effluent liquids which are troublesome if they are discharged into a sewage system. The removal of calcium from blood and its replacement by sodium in order to diminish the tendency of the blood to clot is an interesting medical application. Sometimes the removal of metals is a little more complicated because they do not exist as positively charged ions in solution. For example, ferric chloride in a strong solution of hydrochloric acid exists as a complex ion, $HFeCl_4 \rightleftharpoons H^+ + FeCl_4^-$. In order to remove iron from hydrochloric acid, therefore, a positively charged resin is needed. Similarly gold may be removed from very dilute cyanide solutions as an alternative to the usual method of recovery involving the use of metallic zinc. But here again gold is in the form of a negative ion, $Au(CN)_2^=$, and the positively charged resin has got to be used. Similarly silver may be recovered from the waste fixing solutions used in photographic processing. Maybe the most spectacular use is in the recovery of uranium salts. The concentration of uranium in its ore is usually relatively small, and the problem is to recover this small precentage in an effective manner when much else is present in solution. Here again ion exchange resin has proved by far to be the most economical way of providing the concentration. Very large, completely automatic plants have been constructed in the ore-producing countries for this purpose. Had it not been for the development of this process the cost of metallic uranium might well have been much greater than it is at the present time, and the cost of running nuclear electric power stations made much higher.

Another growing use of positive and negative resins is in the production of practically ion-free water instead of using the usual distillation method. Two methods are used, depending on the concentration of the ions in the water. Suppose the impurity is sodium chloride, Na^+Cl^-, then the first stage consists of passing the water through an acid resin when the Na^+ ions exchange with the H^+ ions, so that there emerges a very dilute solution of hydrochloric acid. This is now run into a column of a basic resin, that is of the type R^+OH^-. Here the chlorine ions displace the OH^- ions, the net result being the formation of water, $R^+OH^- + H^+Cl^- = R^+Cl^- + H_2O$. In this way both positive and negative ions are removed. The process is called the demineralising of water. Once the column has taken up as much as possible of the ions, the first column is regenerated by washing with an acid and the second with alkali. When the amount of mineral matter to be removed is small, regeneration of the resin is probably not worth while, and it is more convenient to make use of a single column of mixed resins. This latter process has been applied to the problem of producing drinking-water from sea-water in lifeboats. Here the equipment has to be of the simplest design and must be easily used. A cube of the mixed resin is crushed to pellets in a rubber bag and the sea-water added. After a matter of a few minutes the salt-free water is drawn off through a layer of the resin in the bottom of the bag.

These resins may also be made in the form of a membrane in which the resin is embedded in a flexible inert support such as polyethylene. If such a membrane separates two compartments of a cell containing ions in water, then the ions can migrate from one compartment to the other, provided certain conditions are fulfilled. Suppose we have a negatively charged

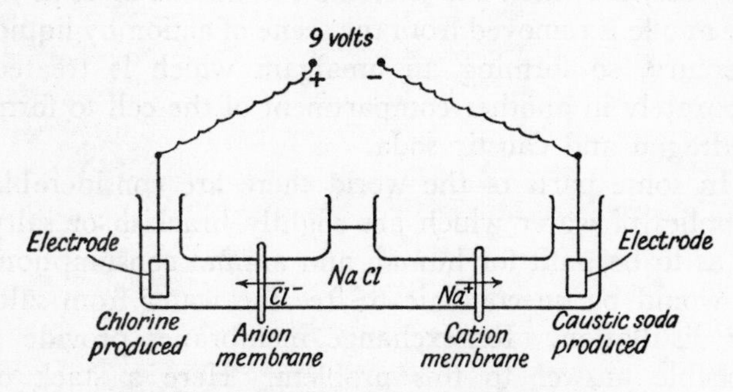

FIG. 33. Ion-exchange membrane apparatus.

membrane containing RSO_3^- groups, and we have an electrolytic cell as shown in figure 33. With sodium chloride in the left-hand compartment, sodium ions would be able to penetrate the membranes, while the chlorine ions would not. This would only happen to a very limited extent because of the development of charges which prevent extensive movement. In the next, more complicated cell there are two membranes, one basic or positively charged, the other acidic or negatively charged. So the first is selectively permeable to a negatively charged ion and the second to positively charged ions. Two electrodes dip into the outer two compartments. When the current is switched on in the direction indicated, the sodium ions move through the membrane to the right, and are discharged at the electrode to produce sodium hydroxide in solution. The chlorine ions move through the membrane to the left and are discharged as chlorine gas at the anode. No sodium ions ever penetrate into this compartment. This is an alternative to the Kastner cell for the production of caustic soda and chlorine, in which the metallic sodium discharged at the anode is removed from the scene of action by liquid mercury, so forming an amalgam which is treated separately in another compartment of the cell to form hydrogen and caustic soda.

In some parts of the world there are considerable supplies of water which are slightly brackish or salty so as to be unfit for human and animal consumption. It would be uneconomic to free the water from salts by distillation. Ion-exchange membranes provide a possible answer to this problem. Here a stack of membranes is constructed alternatively positive and negative. These are connected by pipes to form two alternate sets. An electric potential is applied across the whole stack to make the ions move towards the membranes to which they are permeable. The result is that the water is deprived of both ions in a multistage process and emerges from the stack as pure water. This is all done for a relatively small power input, since the electrical energy is merely needed to move the ions and not to carry out appreciable electrolysis of the system.

Applications of Silicone Resins

Mention has already been made of the silicone resins with a backbone of silicon and oxygen atoms. Since these resins may exist as liquids, greases and rubbers, their applications are extensive. Besides this, they also possess certain quite unique properties which almost put them in a class of their own. The change in properties from liquid to rubber is simply due to an increase in the size of the silicone molecule. The liquids have quite unique properties. The variation of viscosity with temperature is smaller than that of all other liquids and brings them into the same category as the resin-thickened oils. More surprising still is the fact that they are more easily compressible than normal liquids. This compressibility is so great that liquid springs may be made from them. The undercarriage of an aircraft has been made in which the liquid is confined between a tube and a piston so that when the piston receives a sudden load the volume of the silicone fluid decreases appreciably to take it up. The two phenomena are connected, but a perfectly satisfactory explanation has not yet been found. The silicone greases are quite unlike hydrocarbon greases, since they do not become fluid on heating. In fact they remain grease-like in nature until they eventually catch fire and burn, to give silicon dioxide. They can thus be used as lubricants at very much higher temperatures than ordinary greases. When clay is mixed intimately with the grease a putty-like material is obtained. Again it is quite unlike ordinary putty (a mixture of linseed oil and chalk), for if it is rolled into a ball it behaves like rubber, as it bounces up from contact with a hard surface when dropped on it, yet if allowed to remain on the surface for a short period, it flows like a viscous liquid. Similarly the putty breaks if it is suddenly pulled apart—if slowly pulled away it can be drawn into thread, and flows again like a liquid. This is a phenomenon called dilatancy, that is, if the material is subjected to a sudden deformation it tends to break and behaves like a solid, whereas if it is slowly deformed it behaves like a liquid.

Another quite unexpected property is the anti-foam characteristics of the silicones. In some water solutions, for example, of soaps and detergents, foaming can be extremely troublesome. Similarly in many chemical processes foams are produced and are very difficult to disperse. The addition of a few parts per million of a silicone fluid will cut down foaming in a most impressive and remarkable manner. These substances also have anti-stick properties as well. When baking bread and cakes in tins there is often a tendency for the dough to stick to the tin. To prevent this the tins can be coated with greases, but such treatment is only temporary. With silicone treatment, on the other hand, the effect lasts longer and permits the baked article to be removed without difficulty from the tin. Similarly, silicone rubber does not easily stick to coating combinations, glues and sizes, and is therefore specially useful in the textile, paper and other industries. Paper treated with silicones does not adhere or stick to surfaces easily, so much so that even cellophane tape will not stick to it. Paper so treated is also waterproofed in the same way as the fabrics referred to in Chapter 3. Open textured paper like filter paper has the interesting property that if a mixture of petrol and water is poured into such a paper bag, the petrol goes through at once, leaving the water behind. Waterproofing can be applied to masonry to prevent undue penetration of rain or moisture into stone and brickwork in a similar kind of way.

The number of such unusual applications is very great, and many more will no doubt be found for this extremely interesting class of substances.

INDEX